The Life & Ministry of Jesus Christ

From His Preexistence and Birth Through His Galilean Ministry

BOOK ONE

EDITOR: Barbara Munson

NAVPRESS
A MINISTRY OF THE NAVIGATORS

CONTENTS

Introduction

LUKE in his introduction to the Book of Acts, said, "The first account I composed . . . about all that Jesus began to do and to teach, until the day when He was taken up" (Acts 1:1-2). This two-book study, *The Life and Ministry of Jesus Christ*, has been written to help you learn more about Jesus—His teachings (which are an expression of His thoughts), His actions, and His character qualities.

This study emphasizes applying biblical truth to your own life. You who faithfully complete this study should not only have a working knowledge of the life and ministry of Jesus, but a realization that in the process your own life has been changed to become more like Christ's.

> You will think more like Him.
> You will act more like Him.
> His character qualities will have become part of your life.

This study is based on A.T. Robertson's *A Harmony of the Gospels* (Harper & Brothers, 1950) which is printed in chart form on pages 115-117. A harmony arranges the four Gospel accounts of the life of Jesus in parallel form in order to provide one continuous narrative of His life and ministry. Some events, such as the feeding of the five thousand, are recorded in all four Gospels; others appear in only one, such as Jesus' interview with Nicodemus in the Gospel of John. Mark's Gospel is the most chronological (arranged in order of time); the other three, particularly Matthew's, follow a theme or topics rather than a chronology.

Another reason why some events in the Gospels do not seem to appear in chronological order is that Jesus taught the same truths, told the same parables, and performed similar miracles many times in his three-and-a-half-year ministry. For example, Matthew recorded the contents of the Sermon on the Mount in one large section toward the beginning of Jesus' ministry (Matthew 5-7), while Luke wrote down similar teachings of Jesus throughout His ministry (Luke 6:17-49; 11:1-13; 13:22-30). These are not contradictions but records of similar events.

In a Bible study of this type and size, it is impossible to include every incident in the life and ministry of Jesus that is recorded in the Gospels. Although only the major events have been included, the entire study discusses and accounts for all the passages in the four Gospels. The chart at the end of the book lists the passages and the order in which you will study them according to the arrangement in Robertson's harmony.

One of the lasting benefits of this study is that when you have finished both books, you have, in a sense, written your own commentary on the life and ministry of Jesus Christ. These books will serve as a ready reference to the life of Jesus any time you need it. Through your own diligent study you will have done what Bible scholars and commentators do—researched, thought through, and applied the biblical text. In effect, your bookshelf now will hold your own exposition of the life and ministry of Jesus Christ.

Book I traces the life and ministry of Jesus from His preexistence and birth to the Sermon on the Mount, and then to a period of healing and teaching. The nine chapters of this book focus on Jesus early days among men—exciting times with His followers. It begins as a period of popularity in the ministry of the Savior, but ends with serious clashes led by the Pharisees during Christ's Galilean ministry.

You will find that this segment of the life of Jesus contains numerous lessons for your life and ministry today. You will also discover many applications which you can begin putting into practice in your own situation. This section clearly shows Jesus as "He went about doing good, and healing" (Acts 10:38).

How to Do a Chapter

PRAYER should undergird this study on the life and ministry of Jesus Christ. Begin each study time with prayer. Ask the Lord (1) to give you His wisdom and understanding of the spiritual meaning of the Bible passage, and (2) to show you a personal application of the passage—perhaps a change that He wants you to make in your present lifestyle.

Scripture itself—the four Gospels and some verses in Acts 1—is what you will be studying. But because not all the information called for in this study will be found in the Bible, additional reference materials will be helpful. Some suggested ones are:

Reference Materials

1. A reliable Bible dictionary and/or encyclopedia
2. An up-to-date Bible atlas
3. A good Bible handbook
4. A simple commentary
5. An exhaustive concordance
6. A harmony of the Gospels

Some of the above are mentioned and referred to in the bibliography at the end of this workbook.

Each chapter in this book begins with a *map* of a portion of Palestine. To get the feel of what is happening at the location you are studying, complete the map when you begin each chapter. This will also give you an idea of the distances Jesus and His disciples traveled as you actually put yourself "on location." Refer to the map at the back of your book for the location of each city and area. Hardback atlases that highlight Palestine and other historical Bible areas are also available.

The maps in Chapter 1 of Book I and Chapter 7 of Book II are general location maps only, to acquaint you with Jesus' world. The other maps ask you to find specific locations discussed in that particular chapter.

Questions and Charts
The questions and charts in this study are designed to provide factual information as well as to encourage you to dig deeper for the reasons behind the words and actions of Jesus. You will need some creativity of thought in answering some of the "why" and "how" questions and in filling in some of the charts. Not all of the blanks in some charts must necessarily be filled in. In addition, opinion questions are included, which do not necessarily have right or wrong answers but lend themselves well to a stimulating discussion.

Each section in each chapter of this study includes a reference or a series of references from the Gospels. For example:

MARK 6:30-44   JOHN 6:1-13

In this section, Feeding the Five Thousand, you should study both Mark 6:30-44 and John 6:1-13.

Some questions have a number of parts to them, and you should write your answers to these subsections on the line next to the question or statement. For example:

16. Contrast how the disciples and Jesus reacted to the needs of the crowds. (Mark 6:30-44)

DISCIPLES' REACTION (Verses 35-36) _____ *They said that the place was desolate, it*

was quite late, and the people should be sent away to purchase food for themselves.

_____

JESUS' REACTION (Verse 34) _____ *Jesus met the people's spiritual needs. He felt com-*

passion for the multitude and taught them.

_____

(Verses 41-42) _____ *He met their physical needs by miraculously feeding them.*

_____

Since the charts vary considerably, you should follow the specific instructions given for each. None of the charts have vertical lines, so you should write your answers under each of the divisions shown by the instructions at the top.

Personal Application
It is of little value to study the Word of God without applying its teachings to your own life. This study is directed toward personal application in three ways.

1. Specific application questions are included throughout each chapter.

2. Each chapter ends with a section entitled "The Mind of Christ," which discusses what Christ said and did during a particular situation. There are questions such as:

   a. What *action* did Jesus take?
   b. What was His *thinking* behind His action?
   c. What *character quality* did He show?

3. Finally, you will write out one personal application related to some event that occurred in the chapter. You will list specific steps in a plan you will follow, including:

   a. Toward whom will I show this quality?
   b. By what action?
   c. When?
   d. For how long?
   e. What happened, and what changes did I see in my life?

An example of a personal application has been written out on pages 19-20.

The following Christian character qualities are emphasized in Book I of *The Life and Ministry of Jesus Christ.*

Chapter 1—Worshipful and grateful attitude toward the Lord
Chapter 2—Obedience

Chapter 3—Endurance
Chapter 4—Witnessing
Chapter 5—Prayer; dependence upon God
Chapter 6—The nine character qualities from the Sermon on the Mount
Chapter 7—Faith in God
Chapter 8—Doing God's will
Chapter 9—Love for the Lord
       (Jesus' first commandment)

Chapter 1
THE BACKGROUND
TO CHRIST'S COMING

FIRST CENTURY PALESTINE

Locate and label the major geographical areas and cities of first century Palestine.

1. Decapolis
2. Galilee
3. Judea
4. Perea
5. Phoenicia
6. Samaria
7. Syria
8. Bethlehem
9. Caesarea Philippi
10. Capernaum
11. Jerusalem
12. Nazareth

Note:
As you locate the areas and cities on the map, areas should be written in *all capital letters*, and the cities with *only the first letter capitalized.*

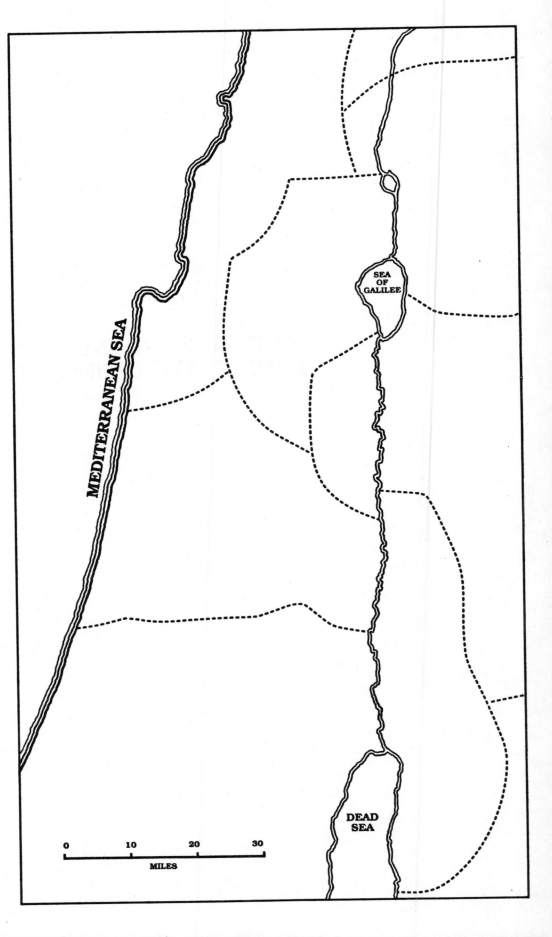

THE BACKGROUND TO CHRIST'S COMING

God, after He spoke long ago to the fathers in the prophets in many portions and in many ways, in these last days has spoken to us in His Son, whom He appointed heir of all things, through whom also He made the world.
HEBREWS 1:1-2

Bible references for this chapter
Matthew 1:1-17; Mark 1:1; Luke 1:1-80; Luke 3:23b-38; John 1:1-18

"The Old Testament is an account of a nation (the Hebrew nation). The New Testament is an account of a Man (the Son of man). The nation was founded and nurtured by God in order to bring the Man into the world (Genesis 12:1-3).

"God Himself became a man so that we might know what to think when we think of God (John 1:14; 14:9). His appearance on the earth is the central event of all history. The Old Testament sets the stage for it. The New Testament describes it. . . .

"The whole Bible is built around the story of Jesus Christ and His promise of life everlasting to men. It was written only that we might believe and understand, know and love, and follow HIM."[1]

The coming of Jesus Christ into human history was the fulfillment of a long line of prophetic statements that started with Genesis 3:15. His arrival in human form was an event planned before the creation of the world (1 Peter 1:20).

The Messiah's Coming Foretold

Ever since man fell in the Garden of Eden from an obedient relationship to God, he has needed a new relationship through a Savior. So God arranged for the coming of the Messiah, His "Anointed One," who would redeem men from their sins. The Old Testament word for "Messiah" is the same as the New Testament word for "Christ."

DEFINITION:
"Anointed One" means one appointed to a specific responsibility.

1. The first promise of a Savior (Jesus Christ) is found in Genesis 3:15. Give the meaning of the four parts of this verse.

MEANING

"I will put enmity between you and the woman,
_____
_____
_____

DEFINITION:
"Enmity" means a deep-seated hatred.

And between your seed and her seed:
_____
_____
_____

He shall bruise you on the head,
_____
_____
_____

MEANING

And you shall bruise him on the heel."

_____

_____

_____

_____

_____

2. What are the main points of the following promise given in the Old Testament?

NATION - ABRAHAM (Genesis 12:1-3; 15:5-6)

Genesis 12:2 _____

_____

Genesis 12:3 _____

_____

_____

QUESTION:
Genesis 15:6 (NIV) says: "Abram believed the Lord, and he credited it to him as righteousness."

Which of God's promises do you claim for your own?

Genesis 15:5 _____

_____

_____

TRIBE - JUDAH (Genesis 49:10)

_____

_____

_____

_____

FAMILY - DAVID (2 Samuel 7:16)

_____

_____

_____

_____

_____

The prophets of Israel provided detailed information about the promised Messiah. True prophecy in the Old Testament did not originate with the prophet, but with God. Isaiah 51:16 says: "And I [the Lord] have put My words in your mouth." God confirmed the ministry of His prophets through the fulfillment of their short-range prophecies. This would indicate that their long-range prophecies concerning the Messiah would also be fulfilled. God's prophets made over 300 prophecies in the Old Testament about Jesus of Nazareth, but we can look at only a few of the highlights.

3. What requirements for the Messiah are set forth in Isaiah 9:6-7?

RACE (NATION OR PEOPLE) _____

_____

SEX _____

_____

TITLES _____

_____

APPLICATION: Has Jesus become all these titles to you personally?

KINGSHIP _____

_____

LENGTH OF RULE _____

_____

CHARACTER OF RULE _____

_____

4. Later, when the wise men came seeking the "King of the Jews" (Matthew 2:2), they were informed by King Herod that according to prophecy the Messiah would be born in Bethlehem of Judea. What makes this prophecy, given approximately 700 B.C., so amazing? (Micah 5:2)

_____

_____

_____

_____

PROPHET, PRIEST, AND KING
Old Testament revelation prophesied that the coming Messiah would be a prophet, a priest, and a king.

The Threefold Office of the Messiah

5. How did the Lord describe the coming Prophet and the role He would fulfill? (Deuteronomy 18:15-19)

Deuteronomy 18:18 _____

(1) PROPHET Speaks the words given to him by God.

_____

_____

_____

How did Jesus fulfill this prophecy? (John 12:49)

_____

_____

Throughout the history of Israel, the priest acted as a mediator between God and man. Animal sacrifices reminded the people that they needed a payment for their sins.

(2) PRIEST
Acts as a person's representative before God by offering up prayers, thanksgivings, and sacrifices.

6. Read Isaiah 52:13-53:12. Note how Jesus Christ, acting as our Priest, offered Himself as the perfect sacrifice for our sins on the Cross.

Isaiah 53:4a _____

_____

Isaiah 53:5a _____

_____

_____

Isaiah 53:6b _____

_____

Who and *where* is our High Priest today? (Hebrews 8:1)

Who _____

_____

Where _____

_____

(3) KING
Possesses supreme power.

7. What was Nathan's prophecy to David regarding the Messiah's kingship? (2 Samuel 7:4-17)

2 Samuel 7:16 _____

_____

_____

_____

The Deity of the Messiah

DEFINITION:
Deity means divine nature or the nature of God.

CROSS REFERENCES:
Philippians 2:6-7
Colossians 1:15-20

JOHN 1:1-18

The beginning of John's Gospel clearly presents the deity of the Messiah.

8. What did John say about Jesus' divinity and preexistence?

John 1:1 _____

_____

_____

John 1:3 _____

_____

John 1:4 _____

_____

_____

9. Why did he present Jesus in this way? (John 20:31)

_____

_____

_____

MATTHEW 1:1-17   LUKE 3:23b-38

The Ancestry of the Messiah

God gave His promises to specific people, so that when Jesus came He would be clearly identified as the Messiah. The divinely planned genealogies in the Gospels of Matthew and Luke give proof to Jesus' claims to the long-promised messiahship.

Matthew traces the legal, or royal ancestry of the Messiah through Joseph, Jesus' legal father, beginning with Abraham. His Gospel was written primarily to the Jews.

Beginning with Adam, Luke traces the physical, or priestly line of Jesus through Mary, His physical mother. His Gospel was written to the Gentiles.

The two genealogies are identical from Abraham to David, where they separate to follow the lines of two of David's sons. They come together again during the Babylonian Captivity with Shealtiel, separating again with the sons of Zerubbabel.

THE GENEALOGY of JESUS CHRIST
(abbreviated form)

LUKE 3:23 (physical line)	MATTHEW 1 (legal line)
Adam	—
Noah	—
Abraham	Abraham
Jacob	Jacob
Judah	Judah
David	David
Nathan	Solomon
Shealtiel	Shealtiel
Zerubbabel	Zerubbabel
Rhesa	Abiud
Heli (Mary's father)	Jacob (Joseph's father)
Mary (Joseph)	Joseph (Mary)
Jesus	Jesus

Generations were often purposely left out, as Matthew did when he arranged his genealogy in groups of fourteen names. Some scholars believe these divisions allowed easier memorization by the early church; others feel the genealogy was divided according to the three periods of Jewish national history. Note: "The son of" can mean either a direct son or a descendant.

Genealogies in Israel were public records, and Jews have never questioned the lineage of Jesus. Many Bible readers skip over these accounts and thus miss some of the interesting people mentioned in the messianic line. A careful study of Matthew's genealogy, for example, shows how God included Jew and Gentile, male and female, saint and sinner in Jesus Christ's lineage.

The Geographic Setting

In order for you to see Jesus in the context of His times, it is important that you know and understand the geography of Palestine during His lifetime. This will help you realize the miles He walked in the hot sun and the physical weariness He experienced. Knowing where Jesus ministered enables you to visualize Him in action.

If you have not already completed the map on page 8, locate the main political areas and major cities of first century Palestine. Note the approximate distances between the cities.

The Men Who Wrote the Gospels

MARK 1:1　　LUKE 1:1-4

As you study the life and ministry of Jesus, you will discover that each of the four Gospels presents a different viewpoint. The first three Gospels are somewhat similar and are called the Synoptic Gospels because of their parallel content. The Gospel of John is different in many ways and contains incidents not found in the other three.

Each Gospel writer, pursuing his own theme, chose to record only certain events from Jesus' life and ministry. When more than one writer chose to include the same event, the accounts often differ in perspective and content. This is not because the writers disagreed on the facts, but because each author had a different relationship to Jesus and a different purpose for writing.

Each writer's background and his relationship to Jesus

10. Give a brief description of each of the following men. Then tell why each was qualified to tell accurately the story of Jesus. (Use a Bible dictionary or handbook.)

Matthew _____

_____

_____

_____

Mark _____

_____

_____

_____

_____

Luke _____

_____

_____

John _____

_____

_____

Because each writer presented Jesus as the Christ to a different group of people, each Gospel contains a different emphasis. The Gospel of Matthew was addressed primarily to Jews and emphasized Jesus as King. Matthew recorded Jesus fulfilling Old Testament prophecies.

The Gospel of Mark was addressed mainly to the Romans and emphasized Jesus as the Servant. Mark recorded the actions of Jesus more than His teachings and concentrated on His power and authority.

The Gospel of Luke was written to the Greeks or Gentiles and emphasized Jesus as a true Man. It presented the human side of the Son of God.

The Gospel of John was addressed to the world and emphasized Jesus as God. The writer built belief in Jesus as the incarnate Son of God and presented Jesus' teachings more than His actions.

Emphasis of each book and to whom written

11. How do the opening words of each Gospel help explain the author's purpose in writing?

Purpose for writing each book

Matthew 1:1,16 _____

_____

_____

_____

Mark 1:1 _____

_____

_____

Luke 1:3-4 _____

_____

_____

_____

John 1:1-4; 20:30-31 _____

_____

_____

_____

_____

God had been strangely silent for some 400 years. Neither angels nor prophets had spoken to men during that period. Now the silence was broken as angels appeared with promises from God. The "fulness of the time" (Galatians 4:4, KJV) had finally arrived, and the Messiah and His forerunner, John the Baptist, were about to appear. (Watch for similarities in the announcements of the angels concerning the births of John the Baptist and Jesus.)

Two Promises

The Promise to Zacharias and Elizabeth

LUKE 1:5-25

"Zacharias was a member of one of the twenty-four divisions of priests who maintained the Temple ritual (1 Chronicles). They took turns in conducting the ceremonies of worship, and each member usually had the privilege of presiding once in his lifetime. The opportunity of offering incense was the high point of Zacharias' career, for he was delegated to enter into the holy place of the Temple where the altar of incense stood before the mysterious veil that concealed the Holy of Holies."[2]

QUESTION:
How does one become "righteous before God" in our day?

12. Describe the character of Zacharias and Elizabeth.

Luke 1:6 _____

_____

_____

Zacharias and Elizabeth were old and childless. This barrenness was considered to be a cause of shame among the Jews. The rabbis went even further, stating that "a childless man should be thought of as dead."

For the Jews, children were considered as a blessing and as the highest form of wealth. Psalm 127 says, "Behold, children are a gift of the Lord; the fruit of the womb is a reward."

QUESTION:
How do you react to a deep disappointment?

13. How had Zacharias and Elizabeth responded to the shame of childlessness? (Luke 1:13-25)

Luke 1:13 _____

_____

Luke 1:25 _____

_____

EXTRA ACTIVITY:
Do a study on angels.

14. While at the altar of incense in the temple, Zacharias was visited by an angel of the Lord who told him that he and his wife, Elizabeth, would have a son. What unusual things would this promised son accomplish?

Luke 1:16 _____

_____

Luke 1:17 _____

_____

_____

The Promise to Mary

LUKE 1:26-38

Luke probably talked with Mary personally before he wrote his account which tells of her deep inward experiences, her calling, her fears, her submission, and her outburst of joy.

15. What were the main points of the angel's message?

Luke 1:31 _____

_____

Luke 1:32-33 _____

_____

_____

_____

16. Record the progressive changes in Mary's attitude as she listened to the angel's message.

Luke 1:29 _____

_____

Luke 1:30 _____

_____

Luke 1:34 _____

_____

Luke 1:38 _____

_____

_____

QUESTION:
What does Luke 1:37 mean to you personally?

QUESTION:
Compared to Mary's example in Luke 1:38, how well do you accept God's will?

Mary Visits Elizabeth

LUKE 1:39-56

Shortly after the angel's appearance, Mary spent three months visiting her relative Elizabeth. The unusual experiences of both women created a special relationship between them.

17. How did Elizabeth greet Mary? (Luke 1:41-43)

_____

_____

_____

What was the meaning behind her words?

_____

_____

_____

_____

18. How was the prophecy about John (Luke 1:15) fulfilled in Luke 1:41-44?

_____

_____

_____

QUESTION:
What do you talk about when you are with your friends? At work? At home?

19. Who (and what) was the focus of their conversation? (Luke 1:46-55)

_____

_____

20. What can you learn from the conversation between Mary and Elizabeth that you can apply to the relationships you have with other people?

_____

_____

_____

John's Birth

LUKE 1:57-80

Because Zacharias and Elizabeth had been childless for such a long time, John's birth was an event of special joy for them. The name, John, assigned by the angel earlier, means, "God has been gracious."

21. Why do you think God wanted the child to be named John?

Luke 1:13 _____

_____

Luke 1:57-58 _____

_____

22. Summarize what Zacharias prophesied about Jesus. (Luke 1:67-75)

Luke 1:68 _____

_____

Luke 1:69 _____

_____

23. Summarize what he prophesied about John. (Luke 1:76-79)

Luke 1:76 _____

_____

Luke 1:76-77 _____

_____

_____

_____

THE MIND OF CHRIST

Isaiah 55:8-9 says:

> "For My thoughts are not your thoughts,
> Neither are your ways My ways," declares the Lord.
> "For as the heavens are higher than the earth,
> So are My ways higher than your ways,
> And My thoughts than your thoughts."

To think and act as the Lord Jesus Christ thinks and acts is completely contrary to the natural man. At the end of each chapter in this study of *The Life and Ministry of Jesus Christ*, you are going to reexamine one particular incident in Jesus' life, emphasizing:

His *ACTIONS*

His *THOUGHTS* behind the actions

His *CHARACTER*

As your study of Jesus continues through the coming months—*and if you pray to this end*—you will discover that your *thinking* process is becoming more and more like Jesus' and less and less like the world's.

Your study of the *thoughts, actions*, and *character* of Jesus will begin in the next chapter.

Chapter Summary

*OUR SPIRITUAL GOAL:
"Let this mind be in you, which was also in Christ Jesus." (Philippians 2:5, KJV)*

PERSONAL APPLICATION

Reread question 20 of this chapter. The focus of the conversation between Mary and Elizabeth was the Lord—praising Him for all the great things He had done in the past and was doing in the present.

How can you develop a *more worshipful and grateful attitude* toward the Lord? Plan an activity and then write down the specific steps you took in fulfilling this activity. (Note: An example has been written for you to follow.)

Toward whom did I show a worshipful and grateful attitude? _____

_____

By what action? _____ *I wrote a list of specific ways in which the Lord has blessed me and is blessing me, and I thanked Him and praised Him for each blessing.*

_____

When? _____ *Every evening after supper, I reread my list of blessings and praised the Lord for each one.*

_____

For how long? _____ *For one week*

What happened? What changes did I see in my life?

My activity has made me much more appreciative toward the Lord and what He is

doing in my life. I had been taking too many things for granted, including the Lord Himself and

His moment-by-moment care for me. Now I am thanking Him frequently throughout the day,

both for the "good" things and the "bad" things because I know they all fulfill some purpose the

Lord has for my life.

My List of Blessings

Friends who love me enough to challenge me when they know I am out of line.

The people in my family, who mean a lot to me.

To be able to attend a church that is building up my faith in God and teaching me how to

become more and more like Jesus.

(Note: The list should continue and include trials and hurts that God has sent to test your faith and produce endurance, according to James 1:2-4.)

Footnotes:
1. Henrietta C. Mears, *What the Bible Is All About* (Glendale, California: Gospel Light Publications, 1966), pages 12-13.
2. Merrill C. Tenney, *New Testament Times* (Grand Rapids, Michigan: William B. Eerdmans Publishing Company, 1965), page 139.

Chapter 2
JESUS' BIRTH AND CHILDHOOD

EARLY TRAVELS

Locate and label (*using capital letters*) the major geographical areas of DECAPOLIS, GALILEE, JUDEA, PEREA and SAMARIA.

Read each Bible reference and write in the name of the city or area where the event took place. Then locate and label it on the map.

You may use small arrows to indicate the travels of Jesus.

1. Jesus' birth and visit of the shepherds (Luke 2:4-7,15)

   _____

2. Presentation at the temple (Luke 2:22)

   _____

3. Visit of the wise men (Matthew 2:8-12)

   _____

4. Flight from Palestine (Matthew 2:13-15)

   _____

5. Childhood home of Jesus (Matthew 2:19-23)

   _____

6. Interview with the teachers (Luke 2:41-46)

   _____

7. Return to His home (Luke 2:51)

   _____

Note: There are approximately eighty miles between Nazareth and Jerusalem, a three-day journey.

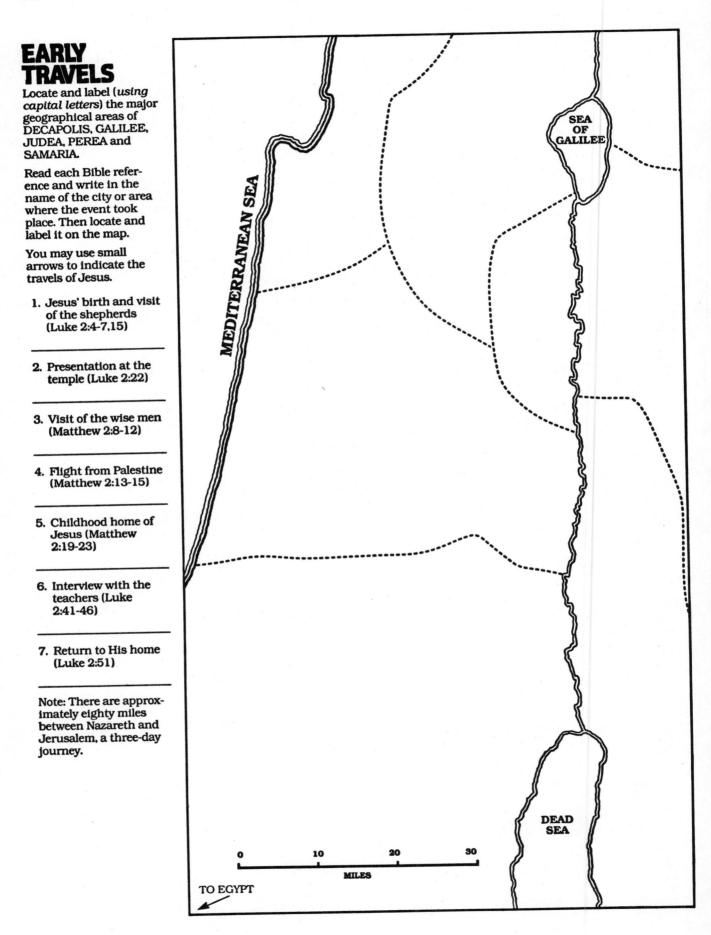

MEDITERRANEAN SEA

SEA OF GALILEE

DEAD SEA

0   10   20   30

MILES

TO EGYPT

JESUS' BIRTH AND CHILDHOOD

But when the fulness of the time came, God sent forth His Son, born of a woman, born under the Law.
GALATIANS 4:4

Bible references for this chapter
Matthew 1:18-2:23; Luke 2:1-52

God chose the perfect time for the arrival on earth of His Son, the promised Messiah. The world was characterized by:

1. *World centralization*—the world-wide Roman Empire which prepared the nations for Christianity by blending them together.

2. *World cultural unity*—a mixing of Romans, Greeks, Orientals, and Jews in all major cities, with Greek becoming the common language.

3. *World trade*—a great system of roads which knit together the whole Roman Empire and aided the eventual spread of Christianity.

4. *World peace*—Pax Romana ("Roman peace"), the universal peace maintained by the Roman military.

5. *World demoralization*—the moral bankruptcy of the national religions which could not meet man's needs.

6. *World mingling of religions*—people comparing and questioning their own traditions because of Rome allowing religious freedom.[1]

Jesus was born in the city of David, Bethlehem, in fulfillment of Old Testament prophecy (Micah 5:2) during a time when Rome occupied Palestine and Herod the Great was the puppet king of the province of Judea.

MATTHEW 1:18-25

Mary and Joseph

Joseph, betrothed to Mary, learned that she was expecting a child. Betrothal with the ancient Hebrews was far more formal and binding than an "engagement" to be married is today. In fact, the betrothed parties were considered legally married. If the bridegroom broke the betrothal contract, the young woman could not be married to another man until she had a paper of divorce. Betrothal was a binding relationship; unfaithfulness was considered adultery.[2]

1. Read Deuteronomy 22:23-27. What were Joseph's alternatives regarding Mary?

Deuteronomy 22:23-24 _____

_____

Matthew 1:19 _____

_____

_____

Instead of these two alternatives, Joseph took Mary as his wife. (Matthew 1:24)

2. What factor caused him to make this decision? (Matthew 1:20-21)

_____

_____

_____

_____

_____

Jesus' Birth

LUKE 2:1-20

"In order to collect taxes effectively, the Romans required a census to be taken the year Jesus was born. Had Judea been then, as in later days, a mere province, her census would have been taken after the Roman method, which enrolled the people wherever they chanced to reside; but since she was still a kingdom, it was taken after the Jewish method, which required each to return to his ancestral seat. . . . Since Joseph was 'of the house and ancestry of David,' he had to travel to Bethlehem, David's city, a three days' journey from Nazareth. And, because of her condition, he took Mary with him, not caring . . . to leave her amid curious and ill-judging people."[3]

3. How is the sovereignty of God shown in the circumstances surrounding Jesus' birth? (Luke 2:1-7; Micah 5:2)

_____

_____

_____

_____

4. According to John's record, what was so special about Jesus? (John 1:1-14)

Verse 1 _____

_____

Verse 3 _____

_____

Verse 4 _____

_____

Verse 12 _____

_____

_____

Verse 14 _____

_____

5. Angels appeared to nearby shepherds announcing Jesus' birth. How did the shepherds respond in each of the following passages?

Luke 2:9 _____

_____

Luke 2:15-16 _____

_____

_____

Luke 2:17 _____

_____

Luke 2:20 _____

_____

*QUESTION:
Why do you think the angels appeared to the shepherds rather than to some other class of people?*

The Bible records only three incidents in Jesus' infancy: His presentation at the temple, the visit of the wise men, and the flight into Egypt.

Jesus' Infancy

PRESENTATION AT THE TEMPLE

LUKE 2:21-39a

6. For what purpose did Joseph and Mary go to the temple? (Luke 2:21-24)

Verse 22 _____

_____

Verse 24 _____

_____

_____

7. Who was Simeon? (Luke 2:25-26)

_____

_____

What special message had the Holy Spirit given Simeon?

_____

_____

_____

8. Summarize what Simeon prophesied about Jesus. (Luke 2:30-33)

_____

_____

_____

9. What was Simeon's prophecy to Mary? (Luke 2:34-35)

_____

_____

_____

_____

10. Who was Anna? (Luke 2:36-37)

_____

_____

_____

11. List some lessons you can learn from Anna's life. (Luke 2:37-38)

_____

_____

_____

_____

_____

_____

VISIT OF THE WISE MEN

MATTHEW 2:1-12

The wise men are sometimes called magi, from the term *magus*, meaning "wizard." "These men in all likelihood came from Persia, and had devoted their lives to the study of the stars. . . . Israel had been under Persian rule, and there is no doubt that the men of Persia had become acquainted with much of the religion and hope of the Hebrew. . . . In all probability they knew the prophecy about the star out of Jacob, the sceptre out of Judah. They knew that this star indicated the birth of a King, so that when they came they said, 'Where is He that is born King of the Jews, for we saw His star in the east, and are come to worship Him?'"[4]

The magi sought this information from Herod, not knowing of his evil reputation. Herod's private life was unsavory, and characterized by cruelty. Over the years he killed two of his ten wives, at least three sons, a brother-in-law, and a wife's grandfather. When he himself was about to die, knowing that the people would rejoice at his death, he commanded that the leading Jews be shut up in the arena at Jericho and be put to death when he died. Thus he craftily planned that though there would be no mourning *for* his death, there would be mourning *at* his death. Fortunately, however, when the news of his death in 4 B.C. arrived, these prisoners were set free.[5]

12. How did Herod learn where the Christ was to be born? (Matthew 2:4-8)

_____

_____

_____

13. What emotions did the magi feel when they reached the Christ Child? (Matthew 2:10-11)

_____

_____

EXTRA ACTIVITY:
Do a study on the gifts given to Jesus—the gold, frankincense and myrrh.

QUESTION:
What gifts does the Lord want from you? Read Micah 6:6-8 and Romans 12:1.

14. Why did the magi not return to Herod although he had requested it? (Matthew 2:12)

_____

_____

15. What personal applications can you learn from the lives and actions of the wise men?

Verses 1-2 _____

_____

_____

Verse 2 _____

_____

_____

Verse 11 _____

_____

_____

FLIGHT INTO EGYPT

MATTHEW 2:13-23

The safety of the Baby Jesus and His mother were concerns of both God and Joseph. Whether the gifts of the wise men financed their escape is not known, but for an undetermined period of time Joseph and his family remained in Egypt. The nearest place of safety to which Joseph could flee with his family was Egypt. Tradition says they penetrated more than a hundred miles within the country and lived there for a year in a Jewish colony. There were more than a million Jews in Egypt at this time, and the colony was highly respectable and influential in the country.[6]

16. How far was Egypt from Bethlehem?

_____

_____

17. Why did Joseph flee to Egypt with his family? (Matthew 2:13)

_____

_____

_____

18. What horrible deed is recorded in Matthew 2:16?

_____

_____

_____

PROPHECY OF HOSEA 11:1b—"Out of Egypt I called My Son."

MATTHEW 2:23b—"He shall be called a Nazarene."

The death of Herod in 4 B.C. signaled the return of Joseph and his family to Palestine. However, since Herod's cruel son Archelaus now reigned in Judea, God directed Joseph to withdraw to Nazareth in Galilee (Matthew 2:22). Matthew views their return from Egypt as the fulfillment of Hosea 11:1, and the settling in Nazareth as fulfilling the prophecy of Christ's lowly estate (Matthew 2:23).

19. Using the following chronological list, briefly state why Joseph and his family visited and lived in each place.

NAZARETH _____

_____

BETHLEHEM _____

_____

JERUSALEM _____

_____

BETHLEHEM _____

_____

EGYPT _____

_____

_____

NAZARETH _____

_____

_____

Jesus' Youth

LUKE 2:39b-52

The Gospels are silent regarding incidents of Jesus' life between His return from Egypt and His baptism at age 30, except for one incident during His visit to the temple when He was 12 years old. This silence further emphasizes the fact that the Gospels are a history of the Savior, not a biography of Jesus of Nazareth.

Nazareth was not an isolated Jewish city, for it was located on one of the major trade routes from the cities on the coast to the cities of the Decapolis to the east (see map on page 8). Due to the strategic location of the city, its citizens were well aware of the cosmopolitan culture of the Gentiles around them as well as of their own more restricted Jewish culture. They were also up-to-date about what was happening in distant places within the Roman Empire.

20. What do you think made up a major part of Jesus' education? (Deuteronomy 6:4-7)

_____

_____

21. In what ways was Jesus' youth normal? (Luke 2:39b-40)

_____

_____

22. In what ways was He exceptional (special or unusual)?

Luke 2:40 _____

_____

_____

Luke 2:46-47 _____

_____

_____

Following the Feast of the Passover, Jesus' parents began their journey home. When they realized Jesus was missing from the caravan, they began a search in Jerusalem which ended three days later in the temple.

23. What is the significance (important meaning) of Jesus' response to His parents? (Luke 2:49)

"I had to be" _____

_____

"In My Father's house" _____

_____

_____

Jesus' visit to the temple in Jerusalem "had a special significance, since the age of twelve marked His becoming *bar-mitzvah*, 'a son of the law.' At that point the Jewish boy reached the age of accountability [answerability] and was formally inducted into the privileges and responsibilities of the community."[7]

THE MIND OF CHRIST

Read Luke 2:46-47 again and consider the thoughts, ways (actions), and character of Jesus as shown in these verses.

1. What was Jesus doing?

_____

_____

Chapter Summary

Our Spiritual Goal:
"Let this mind be in you, which was also in Christ Jesus." (Philippians 2:5, KJV)

Why was He doing this? (What was His thinking behind His action?) (Deuteronomy 4:1-2; 6:6-7; Psalm 1:1-3; 119:11)

_____

_____

_____

3. What character quality did He show?

_____

_____

4. Why do you need to be diligently studying God's Word? (John 14:15, 23)

_____

_____

_____

PERSONAL APPLICATION

Describe how each of the following people showed *obedience* to God.

Zacharias and Elizabeth (Luke 1:6) _____

_____

_____

Joseph (Matthew 1:20, 24) _____

_____

_____

Mary (Luke 1:35, 38) _____

_____

_____

The Shepherds (Luke 2:15) _____

_____

_____

The Wise Men (Matthew 2:12) _____

_____

_____

How can you develop this trait of *obedience* in your own life?

Plan an activity and then write down the specific steps you took in fulfilling this activity.

What action did I take?

When?

For how long?

What happened? What changes did I see in my life?

(See pages 19-20 for an example of a personal application.)

Samuel to King Saul (around 1030 B.C.):

"Has the Lord as much delight in burnt offerings and sacrifices as in obeying the voice of the Lord? Behold, to obey is better than sacrifice."

QUESTION:
How does 1 Samuel 15:22 fit us in the late twentieth century?

Footnotes:

1. Erich Sauer, *The Dawn of World Redemption* (Grand Rapids, Michigan: William B. Eerdmans Publishing Company, 1951), page 176.
2. George B. Eager, "Marriage," *The International Standard Bible Encyclopedia* (Grand Rapids, Michigan: William B. Eerdmans Publishing Company, 1958), pages 1997-1998.
3. David Smith, *The Days of His Flesh* (New York: Harper & Brothers, n.d.), page 3.
4. G. Campbell Morgan, *The Crises of the Christ* (Old Tappan, New Jersey: Fleming H. Revell Company, 1903), pages 98-99.
5. Bruce M. Metzger, *The New Testament, Its Background, Growth, and Content* (New York: Abingdon Press, 1965), page 24.
6. J.W. Shepard, *The Christ of the Gospels* (Grand Rapids, Michigan: William B. Eerdmans Publishing Company, 1939), pages 40-41.
7. Merrill C. Tenney, *New Testament Times* (Grand Rapids, Michigan: William B. Eerdmans Publishing Company, 1965), page 144.

Chapter 3
PREPARATION FOR JESUS' MINISTRY

BEGINNING MINISTRY

Locate and label (*using capital letters*) the major geographical areas of DECAPOLIS, GALILEE, JUDEA, PEREA, and SAMARIA.

Read each Bible reference and write in the name of the city or area where the event took place. Then locate and label it on the map.

You may use small arrows to indicate the travels of Jesus.

1. Last location from previous chapter (Jesus' home)

   _____

2. Baptism by John the Baptist (John 1:28)

   _____

3. Temptation by the devil (Luke 4:1,9)

   _____

4. First miracle of Jesus (John 2:1)

   _____

5. Brief visit with His family (John 2:12)

   _____

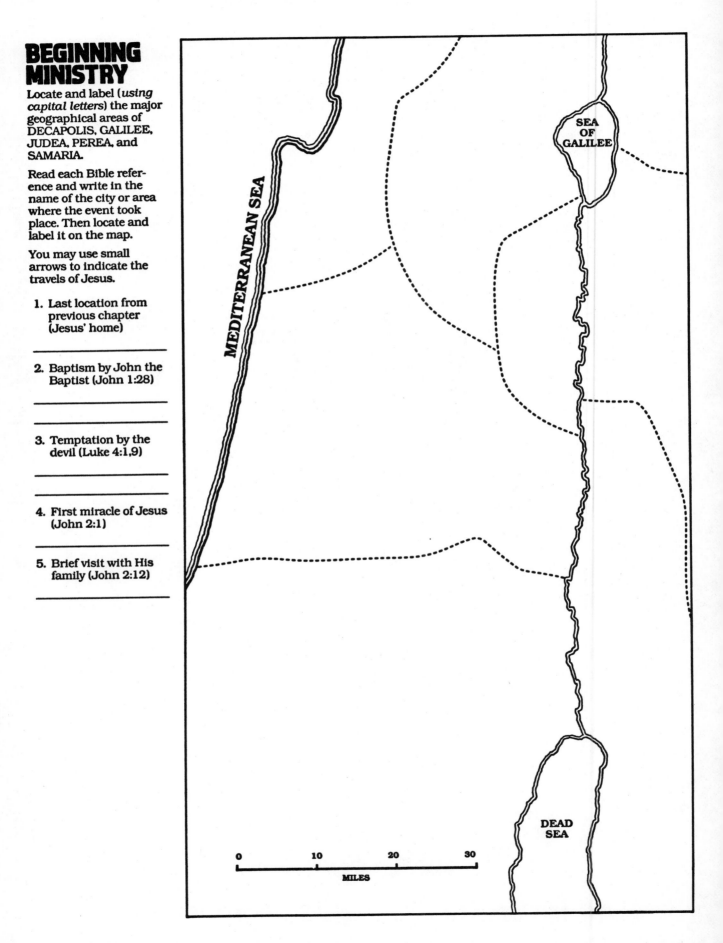

MEDITERRANEAN SEA

SEA OF GALILEE

DEAD SEA

0   10   20   30

MILES

PREPARATION FOR JESUS' MINISTRY

A voice is calling, "Clear the way for the Lord in the wilderness; Make smooth in the desert a highway for our God." ISAIAH 40:3

Bible references for this chapter
   Matthew 3:1-4:11; Mark 1:2-13; Luke 3:1-4:13; John 1:19-2:12

The Messiah did not come unannounced. God could have had the heavens suddenly opened with a heavenly voice announcing to the world His arrival. Or He could have chosen some notable person as the human forerunner. Instead God chose one from among the lowly, one from a humble background.

MATTHEW 3:1-12   MARK 1:2-8

John the Baptist

While Jesus awaited His time in the town of Nazareth, John lived in the desert until he appeared out of the wilderness boldly proclaiming a unique message of repentance. Descended from the priestly line of Aaron, John could have become a priest; but instead, God destined him to become the prophet of whom Malachi had written, "Behold, I am going to send My messenger, and he will clear the way before Me." (Malachi 3:1)

1. Describe John the Baptist's physical appearance and food. (Matthew 3:4)

_____

_____

_____

2. What was John's message? (Matthew 3:2,6)

_____

_____

DEFINITION: Repentance means to change your mind about sin—to see it as God sees it—and turn from it.

How did the people show obedience to this message? (Matthew 3:6)

_____

_____

Note: Outward cleansing (baptism) indicated an inward cleansing (repentance).

3. What character traits do you see in John?

CHARACTER TRAIT   EVIDENCE OF THIS TRAIT

Mark 1:6

_____   _____

_____   _____

CHARACTER TRAIT	EVIDENCE OF THIS TRAIT

Mark 1:7

_____   _____

_____   _____

_____   _____

4. What two things did John say about Jesus? (Matthew 3:11)

a. _____

_____

b. _____

_____

5. How would you have responded to John if you had seen and heard him?

_____

_____

_____

Why? _____

_____

_____

_____

Baptism of Jesus

MATTHEW 3:13-17

When God first gave the Law to Moses, He commanded that certain washings and purification ceremonies be followed.

Because the Pharisees carried out the practice of ceremonial washing or baptism without a genuine, inner change of heart, Jesus later severely rebuked them for their hypocrisy (see Matthew 23:24).

6. What was the meaning behind John's baptism? (See Acts 19:4.)

a. _____

b. _____

_____

7. What did John mean when he said to Jesus, "I have need to be baptized by you"? (Matthew 3:14)

_____

_____

_____

8. Why did Jesus want to be baptized by John? (Matthew 3:15)

_____

_____

_____

Note: Some Bible scholars consider Jesus' baptism as the formal beginning of His public ministry.

9. What did the descending of the Holy Spirit on Jesus indicate to John? (John 1:33-34)

_____

_____

_____

_____

_____

_____

10. How was the Trinity of God shown? (Matthew 3:16-17)

_____

_____

_____

_____

MATTHEW 4:1-11

Temptation in the Wilderness

Immediately following Jesus' baptism, the Holy Spirit led Him into the wilderness of Judea to be confronted by the devil (Satan).

11. What statement from God did the devil question in two of the three temptations? (Compare Matthew 3:17 with Matthew 4:3 and 4:6.)

_____

_____

_____

_____

12. What false idea did the devil have about Jesus as shown in these three temptations?

_____

_____

13. In each of His responses to the devil, Jesus quoted from the book of Deuteronomy. We can more fully understand each temptation as we discover why Jesus quoted that particular passage. Complete the following chart.

QUESTION:
Be honest! Which would you value the most—spending thirty minutes eating your favorite meal or thirty minutes meditating upon God's Word?

What are your priorities?

TEMPTATION	WHAT THE PASSAGE SAYS	WHAT THIS PASSAGE MEANS
Turn rock into bread	Deuteronomy 8:3a	
Leap off pinnacle	Deuteronomy 6:16a	
Worship Satan	Deuteronomy 6:13	

14. How did Jesus prepare Himself through the years to meet these temptations?

_____

_____

15. Describe how the devil misquoted Scripture. (Compare Psalm 91:11-12 with Matthew 4:6.)

_____

_____

16. What does this reveal about the devil?

_____

_____

17. Why do you think this event and its timing are important? (Consider Jesus' ultimate purpose for coming to earth.)

_____

_____

_____

_____

18. What is Jesus' attitude toward us when we face temptations? Why? (See Hebrews 4:15.)

_____

_____

_____

JOHN 1:35-51

Jesus' Early Followers

When Jesus came out of the wilderness after the temptation, John pointed Him out as the One whose coming he had been announcing.

19. What did John mean when he said, "Behold, the Lamb of God who takes away the sin of the world"? (John 1:29 and 36)

_____

_____

_____

20. John then introduced Jesus to some of his own disciples who immediately became Jesus' followers. Complete the following chart. (Not every blank will be filled.)

FOLLOWER	HOW HE MET JESUS	WHAT HE CALLED JESUS	WHY HE FOLLOWED HIM
The two disciples (John and Andrew) (verses 35-36)			

FOLLOWER	HOW HE MET JESUS	WHAT HE CALLED JESUS	WHY HE FOLLOWED HIM
Peter (verses 40-42)			
Philip (verses 43-45)			
Nathanael (verses 45-50)			

QUESTION:
In what way should you model your life after Andrew and Philip?

What attracts people to Jesus today? What attracted you to Him?

_____

_____

_____

_____

_____

_____

_____

_____

_____

_____

_____

_____

Wedding at Cana

JOHN 2:1-12

Three days after His conversation with Nathanael, Jesus, His mother, and His new followers attended a wedding feast in Cana of Galilee. Here Jesus performed His first miracle.

"On the evening of the marriage, the bride was led from her paternal home to that of her husband, accompanied by music with the distribution of oil and wine among friends and nuts among the children, and led by the 'friends of the bridegroom, who bore torches and lamps, myrtle branches and chaplets of flowers.' The veiled bride on arrival was led to the bridegroom, the marriage formula pronounced, the legal documents signed. This was followed by the washing of the hands, and finally the marriage feast, which might last a day and sometimes a week."[1]

During this wedding feast, the wine ran out, and Jesus' mother presented the problem to her Son. (Wine used in Palestine during this time was mixed with three parts of water.) Jesus turned the water in the large jars into wine, and the new wine was brought to the master of the banquet. It was his duty to superintend the feast, including examining and tasting everything before it was served. He was surprised that the "good wine" had been saved rather than being served at the beginning.

21. Why do you think Jesus was willing to change the water into wine when He was unwilling to turn the stones into bread in the wilderness?

_____

_____

_____

QUESTION:
What is a miracle? Do miracles still occur today?

22. Why was this first miracle particularly important? (John 2:11)

_____

_____

_____

DEFINITION OF A MIRACLE:
Adult definition: A supernatural act of divine power. Kindergartener's definition: Something only God can do!

23. How is Jesus shown to be the Son of God in this episode?

_____

_____

_____

After this spectacular, though private, miracle, Jesus and His family spent a few days in Capernaum, a city which would become His center of operations in the future. The time was now right for the beginning of His public ministry.

THE MIND OF CHRIST

Reread Matthew 4:1-11 and consider the thoughts, ways (actions), and character of Jesus. Satan tempted Jesus in the areas of hunger, power and glory, and trust in His heavenly Father. If Jesus had compromised and fallen under Satan's temptations, He would have become a sinner like us and unable to go to the cross for our sins.

1. What was Jesus doing in this passage (Matthew 4:1-11) which follows the principles stated in Ephesians 6:10-13?

_____

_____

_____

Chapter Summary

OUR SPIRITUAL GOAL:
Let this mind be in you, which was also in Christ Jesus. (Philippians 2:5, KJV)

2. Why? (What was He thinking as He resisted Satan?) (Hebrews 12:2)

_____

_____

_____

3. What character quality did He show? (Hebrews 12:1-3)

_____

4. How can you follow Jesus' example today? (Hebrews 12:1-3)

Verse 1 _____

_____

Verse 2 _____

_____

Verse 3 _____

_____

Ephesians 6:11 _____

_____

PERSONAL APPLICATION

One definition for *endurance (perseverance)* could be:

> Standing strong through all trials, knowing that they are for
> the purpose of maturing me in my Christian walk.

How can you develop this trait of *endurance* through some trial you are
experiencing?

Plan an activity and then write down the specific steps you took in fulfilling this
activity. (See pages 19-20 for an example.)

Toward whom (or what) did I show endurance?

What action did I take?

When did I take this action?

For how long?

What happened? What changes did I see in my life?

Footnote
1. J. W. Shepard, *The Christ of the Gospels* (Grand Rapids, Michigan: William B. Eerdmans Publishing Company, 1939), pages 88-89.

Chapter 4
JESUS' MANIFESTATION
TO ISRAEL

ACTIONS AND DIALOGUES

Locate and label (*using capital letters*) the major geographical areas of DECAPOLIS, GALILEE, JUDEA, PEREA, and SAMARIA.

Read each Bible reference and write in the name of the city or area where the event took place. Then locate and label it on the map.

You may use small arrows to indicate the travels of Jesus.

1. Last location from previous chapter

———————————

2. Cleansing of the temple (John 2:13-15)

———————————

3. Interview with Nicodemus (John 3:1-2; 2:23)

———————————

4. Traveling with His disciples (John 3:22)

———————————

5. Location of John's baptizing (John 3:23)

———————————

6. Discussion with the woman at the well (John 4:4-7)

———————————

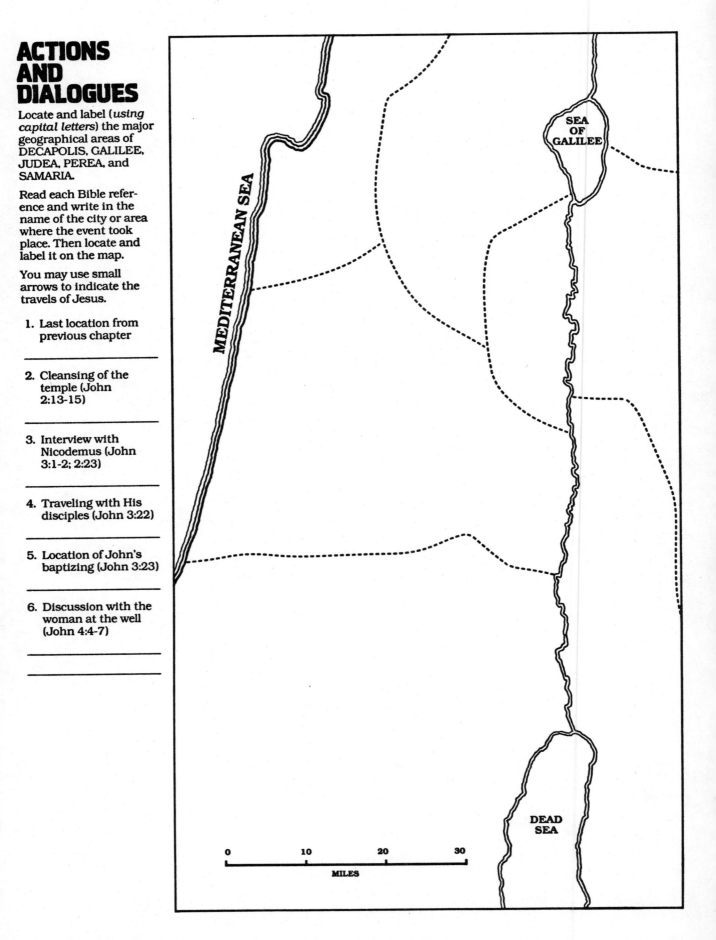

JESUS' MANIFESTATION TO ISRAEL

Many other signs therefore Jesus also performed in the presence of the disciples, which are not written in this book; but these have been written that you may believe that Jesus is the Christ, the Son of God; and that believing you may have life in His name.
JOHN 20:30-31

Bible references for this chapter
John 2:13-4:42

Jesus Christ's public ministry took place during a three-year period that centered around four Passovers. (See the chart at the back of this workbook.) He began His ministry during the first of these Passovers; in it He presented Himself as the Promised Messiah in the cleansing of the temple, which was His Father's house. He was crucified and rose again during the period of the fourth Passover. Between these two points in time (A.D. 27-30), He ministered publicly.

Since the age of twelve, Jesus had made the annual journey to Jerusalem from Galilee. Now it was not the mere custom of the Feast that took Him to Jerusalem to present Himself as the Messiah. His first appeal was to the rulers of the nation.

Up to this point Jesus had been living as an ordinary carpenter in Nazareth. Only John's Gospel records Jesus' initial ministry in Jerusalem. John, under the guidance of the Holy Spirit, chose to relate the following four events because they helped to show that Jesus was indeed the Son of God.

DEFINITION:
Jesus' manifestation means His revealing Himself as the Son of God and Israel's promised Messiah.

JOHN 2:13-25

First Cleansing of the Temple

Jesus and His disciples traveled from Capernaum to Jerusalem to celebrate the Passover. The activities of this most holy feast were centered in the temple.

1. Read Exodus 12. Describe the events of the first Passover.

_____

_____

_____

_____

_____

A DESCRIPTION OF THE PASSOVER DURING JESUS' TIME

"As Passover approaches, the city throbs with life . . . Pilgrims fill all inns and the hostels attached to synagogues. . . .

"By the evening of 13 Nisan, in the Roman month of April, each house has been cleaned and any leavened bread eaten or burned before the feast—for Passover signals a complete rejuvenation. The following afternoon, sacrifices begin. Families or friends in groups of 10 to 20 join to buy a lamb or kid. Their representatives carry the victim to the temple courtyard and slaughter it. Priests gather the blood in cups, pour it at the foot of the altar, and burn the entrails on the perpetual fire. The sacrificial animal, carried back to the house where the family waits, will be roasted on a rod of pomegranate wood."[1]

The temple, a magnificent structure, was at the center of all Jewish religion. Three temples have been built in Jerusalem on Mt. Moriah—the first one by Solomon, the second by Zerubbabel, and the last by Herod the Great, which stood at the time of Christ. This temple, known as Herod's Temple, was destroyed in 70 A.D. when Jerusalem fell to Rome.

2. Being able to visualize the temple will help in understanding the setting in which Jesus began His public ministry.

    Briefly describe each of the following areas of Herod's Temple, and then locate it on the floor plan on the next page.

a. COURT OF THE GENTILES _____

_____

b. WOMEN'S COURT _____

_____

_____

c. MEN'S COURT _____

_____

d. PRIESTS' COURT _____

_____

e. ALTAR OF BURNT OFFERING _____

_____

_____

f. HOLY PLACE _____

_____

g. HOLY OF HOLIES _____

_____

_____

MONEY-CHANGERS
The profession of money-changer in Palestine was made necessary by the law requiring every male Israelite who had reached the age of 20 years to pay into the treasury of the sanctuary a half-shekel as an offering to Jehovah, with even the poor having to pay. It seems to have become an annual tax and was to be paid in the regular Jewish half-shekel. Since the Jews, coming up to the feasts, would need to exchange their various coins for this Jewish piece, there were money-changers who made the exchange for whatever fee they could charge.

HEROD'S TEMPLE

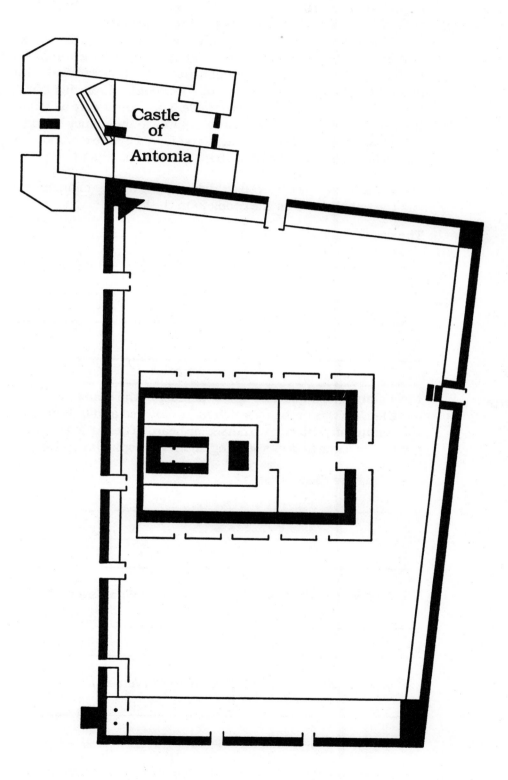

Castle
of
Antonia

SUPERINTENDING PRIESTS

The animals for sacrifices and offerings had to be examined by persons duly appointed. For such inspection there were enormous charges. If a dove or lamb were sold, it would be for five or six times the just price.

By the time Jesus had begun His public ministry, the whole temple operation had become one huge system of graft. It had come into being under the ex-high priest Annas who had dominated the High Priesthood for many years. He had established the corrupt market for the sale of sacrificial animals and the money exchange system in the temple. The profits were all supposed to flow into the Temple treasury, but they went mainly to the money-changers and to superintending priests, who were hated and feared by the common people.[2] (It was Annas before whom Jesus was tried prior to His crucifixion.)

3. What impact would Jesus' driving of the money-changers and traders out of the temple have on the people? On the leaders?

The people _____

_____

The leaders _____

_____

Discussion with Nicodemus

JOHN 3:1-21

Nicodemus was a Pharisee and a member of the Sanhedrin, the ruling body of Judaism. He was probably a rich man, cultured and in high social standing in the community. Having witnessed or heard of Jesus' fearless act of cleansing the temple, he came to Jesus seeking answers to spiritual questions.

4. Who were the Pharisees?

_____

_____

_____

5. Nicodemus addressed Jesus as "Rabbi." What is a rabbi?

_____

_____

6. Who did Nicodemus think Jesus was? (Verse 2)

_____

_____

QUESTION:
If someone asked you to explain the term born again, *could you?*

7. What unusual statement did Jesus make to Nicodemus? (Verse 3)

_____

_____

What did this statement mean spiritually?

_____

_____

_____

8. Why did Nicodemus have trouble understanding what Jesus said? Give two reasons. (See 1 Corinthians 2:12-14.)

a. _____

_____

_____

b. _____

_____

9. How did Jesus' message to Nicodemus in John 3:13-21 identify Christ as the Son of God?

Verse 13 _____

_____

Verses 14-15 _____

_____

Verses 16-18 _____

_____

10. Read Numbers 21:5-9. Explain the relationship between Moses lifting up the bronze serpent on a pole, and Jesus being lifted up on a cross. (Verse 14)

_____

_____

_____

_____

11. What impact did the discussion with Jesus have on Nicodemus?

John 7:43-52, especially verse 51 _____

_____

_____

John 19:38-42 _____

_____

12. What did you learn about eternal life from this passage? (Verse 16)

_____

_____

_____

John the Baptist's Explanation of Jesus

JOHN 3:22-36

After the Passover, Jesus and His disciples began to minister in the Judean countryside, the same area in which John and his disciples were ministering. John's disciples became upset because Jesus' disciples were baptizing more people than they were.

13. How did John compare himself to Jesus?

Verse 28 _____

_____

Verse 29 _____

_____

Verse 30 _____

_____

14. What did John say to his disciples to show them that Jesus was God's Son?

Verse 31 _____

_____

Verse 34 _____

_____

Verse 35 _____

_____

Verse 36 _____

_____

15. What lessons can John's attitude toward Jesus and His increasing ministry teach us?

_____

_____

_____

_____

JOHN 4:1-42

Conversion of the Samaritan Woman

The Pharisees also heard that Jesus was making more disciples than John. When Jesus learned of this, He started back to Galilee, taking the direct route through Samaria. For Jews to travel through Samaria was unusual, and Jesus' conversation with a Samaritan woman was more so.

16. Who were the Samaritans? (See 2 Kings 17:24-29 and reference books.)

_____

_____

_____

_____

Why did the Jews hate the Samaritans?

_____

_____

_____

17. What are some other possible reasons why it would be unusual for Jesus to talk to this woman?

_____

_____

_____

Scripture says that it was about the sixth hour when Jesus arrived at the Well of Jacob in Sychar. The Jewish day began at sunrise, which was called the first hour; it ended at sunset, the twelfth hour. The sixth hour was always noon, the hottest time of the day.

Noon was an unusual time for a woman to be drawing water, and it pointed up the fact that she was an outcast. Besides having serious moral problems (which Jesus uncovered), she was also well-versed in Samaritan religious beliefs and tried to side-track the conversation to a theological discussion.

18. What do you think Jesus meant when He said that men are to worship God "in spirit and in truth"? (John 4:23-24)

"in spirit" _____

_____

_____

"in truth" _____

_____

_____

EXTRA ACTIVITY:
Do a study on "living water." Read Jeremiah 2:13 and John 7:37-39, as well as John 4:10-14. Are you experiencing spiritual thirst?

19. What did Jesus say to this woman about her needs and the answer to these needs?

Verse 10 _____

_____

Verses 13-14 _____

_____

Verses 25-26 _____

_____

20. How did Jesus compare food and doing His Father's will? (John 4:31-34)

_____

_____

_____

_____

21. The Samaritan woman and the Pharisee Nicodemus represented the opposites of the religious, moral, and social order of that day. How were they different?

	NICODEMUS	SAMARITAN WOMAN
Religiously		
Morally		
Socially		

What similar need did they have? _____

_____

22. What specific prejudice (race, religion, or social standing) do you have that must be overcome if you are to copy Jesus' concern for "lost" people?

_____

_____

_____

23. What did the Samaritan woman do when she returned to the city? (John 4:28-30, 39-40)

_____

_____

_____

What was the final result? (John 4:39, 41-42)

_____

_____

THE MIND OF CHRIST

In John 3 and 4, Jesus witnessed to two very different "lost" people, Nicodemus and the Samaritan woman. One was from the upper class of society, the other from the lower. Jesus was equally concerned that each would understand who He was and that He was the way to eternal salvation.

1. What did Jesus *do* in John 3:14-18 and in John 4:10, 14, 25-26?

_____

_____

_____

_____

2. Why did Jesus *think* it was important to witness to these two people? (John 3:16)

_____

_____

3. What *character quality* was Jesus showing?

_____

_____

4. Why is it important for everyone, including you, to follow Jesus' example and witness to others? (Romans 10:13-14)

a. _____

_____

b. _____

_____

c. _____

_____

Chapter Summary

OUR SPIRITUAL GOAL: Let this mind be in you, which was also in Christ Jesus. (Philippians 2:5, KJV)

PERSONAL APPLICATION

The burden that Jesus had for the "lost" should be your burden also. Go to prayer and ask Him to direct you to someone who needs to hear the plan of salvation through faith in Jesus Christ.

Plan an activity and then write down the specific steps you took in fulfilling this activity.

> To whom did I witness?
>
> How did I witness to this person? (What was my plan of action?) When did I take this action?
>
> What happened? What changes did I see in the other person?
>
> What will be my follow-up?

Footnotes:
1. Roland de Vaux, "The World of Jesus," *Everyday Life in Bible Times* (Washington, D.C.: National Geographic Society, 1967), pages 299-300.
2. J.W. Shepard, *The Christ of the Gospels* (Grand Rapids, Michigan: William B. Eerdmans Publishing Company, 1939), page 93.

Chapter 5
AUTHENTICATION OF JESUS' MISSION BY HEALING

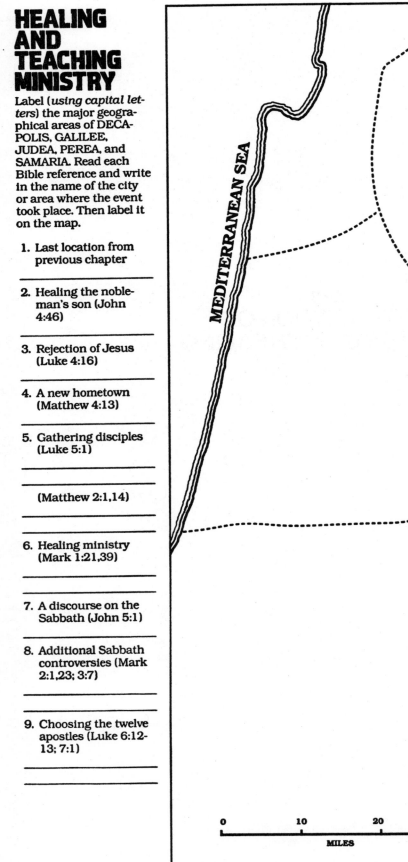

HEALING AND TEACHING MINISTRY

Label (*using capital letters*) the major geographical areas of DECAPOLIS, GALILEE, JUDEA, PEREA, and SAMARIA. Read each Bible reference and write in the name of the city or area where the event took place. Then label it on the map.

1. Last location from previous chapter

   _____

2. Healing the nobleman's son (John 4:46)

   _____

3. Rejection of Jesus (Luke 4:16)

   _____

4. A new hometown (Matthew 4:13)

   _____

5. Gathering disciples (Luke 5:1)

   _____

   _____

   (Matthew 2:1,14)

   _____

   _____

6. Healing ministry (Mark 1:21,39)

   _____

   _____

7. A discourse on the Sabbath (John 5:1)

   _____

8. Additional Sabbath controversies (Mark 2:1,23; 3:7)

   _____

   _____

9. Choosing the twelve apostles (Luke 6:12-13; 7:1)

   _____

   _____

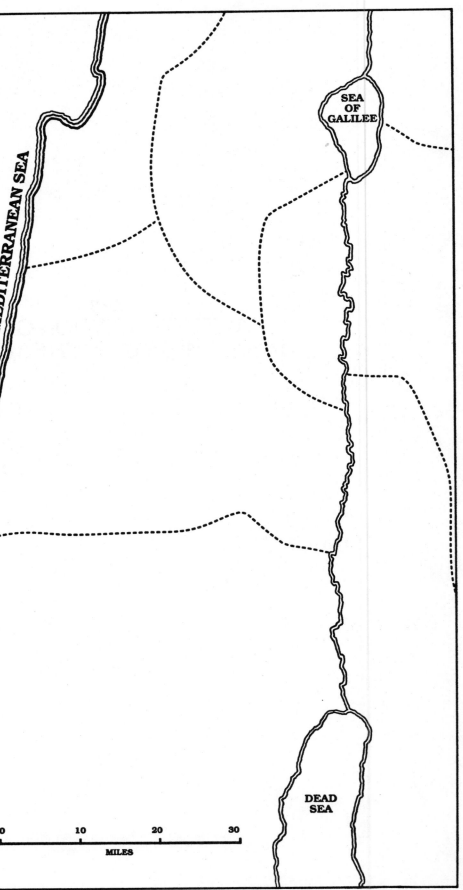

MEDITERRANEAN SEA

SEA OF GALILEE

DEAD SEA

0   10   20   30

MILES

AUTHENTICATION OF JESUS' MISSION BY HEALING

"I will feed My flock and I will lead them to rest," declares the Lord God. "I will seek the lost, bring back the scattered, bind up the broken, and strengthen the sick; but the fat and the strong I will destroy. I will feed them with judgment."
EZEKIEL 34:15-16

Bible references for this chapter
Matthew 4:12-10:4; Mark 1:14-3:19a; Luke 4:14-6:16; John 4:43-5:47

Jesus returned from His ministry in Jerusalem and Samaria to Galilee, the region where He had been raised. The term *Galilee*, taken from the Hebrew word *galil*, means "circle." In this area, surrounded by non-Jewish peoples, Christ chose to begin His extensive ministry, traditionally called the *Great Galilean Ministry*.

DEFINITION: Authentication means to prove that something is true—in this case, proving that Jesus was who He said He was.

The Geographic Setting in Galilee

LUKE 4:14-15

1. Using a Bible dictionary or encyclopedia, write a description of Galilee during the time of Jesus.

SIZE _____

_____

POPULATION _____

_____

CLIMATE _____

_____

PEOPLE _____

_____

_____

PRODUCTS _____

_____

MAJOR CITIES _____

_____

"It seems fitting that Jesus' ministry should find its greatest expression in Galilee. It was the most beautiful, productive and populous district of Palestine. The bright sunny sea of Galilee with its sturdy fisher-folk, surrounded by a beautiful country, was perfect as a setting for His wonderful life and activity.

Jesus liked to mingle in the crowd; He loved human beings. Here He found a dense population made up of all types and nationalities."[1]

Healing the Nobleman's Son

OBSERVATION:
From here on, note the power of Jesus' words.

JOHN 4:46-54

The reports of Jesus' miracles caused a nobleman from Herod's court to go to Cana to ask Jesus to heal his sick son.

2. How did Jesus test the faith of this nobleman? (Verse 50)

_____

_____

How did the man respond to Jesus' test?

_____

_____

3. What happened spiritually as a result of the son being healed? (Verse 53)

_____

_____

_____

Rejection at Nazareth

LUKE 4:16-30

The news about Jesus spread throughout all Galilee. For some time, He preached in the synagogues and was well received. He then visited His hometown of Nazareth, where a different reception awaited Him as He presented His messianic claims in the synagogue.

4. For what reasons did the Jews meet in the synagogues? (Refer to a Bible dictionary or encyclopedia.)

_____

_____

_____

5. Why do you think Jesus chose to read the Isaiah 61:1 passage? (Luke 4:17-21)

OBSERVATION:
Isaiah predicted some specific characteristics of Jesus' ministry— that He would preach, heal, and redeem.

Verse 18 _____

_____

_____

Verse 19 _____

_____

_____

Verse 21 _____

_____

6. What caused the people of Nazareth to be different from other Galileans and to openly oppose Jesus?

Verse 22 _____

_____

7. What explanation did Jesus give for their opposition?

Verse 24 _____

_____

QUESTION:
Why do people oppose Jesus today?

MATTHEW 4:13-17

Move to Capernaum

The opposition in Nazareth caused Jesus to move to Capernaum. This city was located on the northwest shore of the Sea of Galilee. It had a synagogue and probably a Roman military garrison. Jesus selected it as His center of operations, and it became known as "His" city (Matthew 9:1). Later in His ministry He condemned it for its lack of faith and predicted its downfall (Matthew 11:20-24).

8. Why did Jesus make Capernaum His city instead of Nazareth?

_____

_____

How is Jesus' reaction to Nazareth's rejection and Capernaum's acceptance similar to His reaction toward individuals today?

_____

_____

_____

Gathering Disciples

As soon as Jesus had settled in Capernaum, He began preaching the Gospel of the Kingdom and calling disciples to follow Him.

"The expression 'Follow Me' would be readily understood as implying a call to become the permanent disciple of a teacher. It was the practice for a Master to gather around him a circle of disciples, so Peter, Andrew, and the sons of Zebedee would have understood the call of Christ.

"The twelve arrived at their final close relation to Jesus only by degrees through three different stages in their fellowship with Him. In the *first stage* they were simply believers in Him as the Christ and were His occasional companions.

"In the *second stage*, fellowship with Christ assumed the form of an uninterrupted attendance and the abandonment of their secular occupations. . . .

"The twelve entered on the *last and highest stage* of discipleship when they were chosen by their Master as a select band to be trained for the great work of the apostleship."[2]

The Fishermen

MATTHEW 4:18-22   LUKE 5:1-11

9. What attracted these men to Christ? (Luke 5:3 and 6)

_____

_____

_____

10. How does each phrase of Jesus' challenge in Matthew 4:19 apply to us today?

FOLLOW ME _____

_____

_____

EXTRA ACTIVITY:
Compare Jesus' words
in Matthew 4:19 and
John 15:5.

_____

AND I WILL MAKE YOU _____

_____

_____

FISHERS OF MEN _____

_____

_____

The Tax Collector

LUKE 5:27-32

How far Jesus stepped out of traditional Jewish attitudes toward sinners can only be understood in light of the teachings by the rabbis. They knew nothing about forgiveness of sin, free and unconditional. In contrast, Jesus Christ freely invited all repentant sinners to come to Him whatever their past, assuring them of welcome and grace.

QUESTION:
Have you ever been
the only Christian in a
group of non-Chris-
tians? Did you accept
or reject them? Did you
partake of their activi-
ties? How did you
feel?

11. Why were tax collectors despised by most Jews?

_____

_____

_____

12. What do we learn about Jesus from His attitude toward Matthew?

_____

_____

_____

_____

MARK 1:21-2:13

An extensive healing ministry followed. Everywhere Jesus went, people crowded around Him. After healing their sick, Jesus taught them. He aroused the anger of the religious leaders by healing on the Sabbath.

13. What does it mean "to teach with authority"? (Mark 1:21-22)

_____

_____

_____

14. Jesus healed people almost everywhere He went. Fill in the following chart.

REFERENCES/ WHO WAS HEALED OF WHAT	HOW HE WAS HEALED	REASON FOR HEALING	REACTIONS OR RESULTS
Mark 1:21-28 Luke 4:31b-37 A man with an unclean spirit			
Matthew 8:14-17 Mark 1:29-31 Luke 4:38-41 Simon's mother-in-law had a fever.			
Matthew 8:2-4 Mark 1:40-45 Luke 5:12-16 leper			

REFERENCES/ WHO WAS HEALED OF WHAT	HOW HE WAS HEALED	REASON FOR HEALING	REACTIONS OR RESULTS
Matthew 9:1-8	_____	_____	_____
Mark 2:1-13	_____	_____	_____
Luke 5:17-26	_____	_____	_____
paralytic	_____	_____	_____
	_____	_____	_____
	_____	_____	_____
	_____	_____	_____
	_____	_____	_____
	_____	_____	_____
	_____	_____	_____

15. What practical conclusions do you draw from these healings of Jesus?

_____

_____

   The first three healings took place while Jesus was still in Capernaum. He healed the leper and the paralytic after He had set out to visit the towns and villages throughout Galilee (Mark 1:39).

16. What characterized the ministry of Jesus in the midst of great activity?

Mark 1:35-37 _____

_____

_____

Luke 5:16 _____

_____

_____

The Sabbath Controversies

MARK 2:23-3:12   JOHN 5:1-47

Our Lord came into sharp conflict with the religious leaders of the Jews in the matter of Sabbath observance. He set Himself squarely against the restrictions placed on the Sabbath by the rabbis. They believed the Sabbath to be an end in itself and that man was made for the Sabbath. This meant that although man might suffer hardship, the laws relating to the Sabbath had to be kept no matter what.

   Jesus, on the contrary, taught that the Sabbath was made for man's benefit. If there were a conflict between meeting man's needs and following the letter of the Law, Jesus believed that meeting man's needs was of greater importance.

17. Study the passages indicated and fill in the following chart.

THE ISSUE	REACTIONS/ COMMENTS OF THE JEWS	CHRIST'S REBUTTAL	RESULTS	
Verses 8-9	Verse 16	Verse 17	Verse 16	John 5:1-17
_____	_____	_____	_____	
_____	_____	_____	_____	
_____	_____	_____	_____	
_____	_____	_____	_____	
_____	_____	_____	_____	
_____	_____	_____	_____	
	Verse 10			
	_____			
	_____			
	_____			
	_____			
	_____			
Verse 23	Verse 24	Verses 25-26		Mark 2:23-28
_____	_____	_____		
_____	_____	_____		
_____	_____	_____		
_____	_____	_____		
_____	_____	_____		
_____	_____	_____		
		Verse 27		
		_____		
		_____		
		_____		
		_____		
		_____		
Verses 1,2, and 5	Verse 2	Verse 4	Verse 6	Mark 3:1-6
_____	_____	_____	_____	
_____	_____	_____	_____	
_____	_____	_____	_____	
_____	_____	_____	_____	
_____	_____	_____	_____	
_____	_____	_____	_____	

18. How would you compare Christ's attitude with that of the Pharisees?

_____

_____

_____

After these encounters with the Pharisees, Jesus withdrew to the shores of the Sea of Galilee where He healed and taught many.

Choosing the Twelve Apostles

OBSERVATION:
This is a critical event in Jesus' ministry, for these are the men He would be working with; these men are to become disciplemakers.

QUESTION:
What would have been your feelings that day if Jesus had chosen you to be one of the Twelve?

LUKE 6:12-16

Jesus chose twelve men out of all His disciples to be His apostles. There is a difference in the names on the lists of the apostles. Judas, the son of James, is called Thaddeus in Mark, and Lebbaeus in Matthew. Bartholomew is probably Nathanael. Peter stands first in all the lists and Judas Iscariot last. The names are usually arranged in pairs which may refer to their ministering together. The list contains two or three pairs of brothers and at least one pair of close friends—Philip and Nathanael. All except Judas Iscariot were Galileans; Judas was a Judean.

19. What does the word *apostle* mean? (Look in a Bible dictionary.)

_____

_____

20. How does this meaning apply to the Twelve? (See Matthew 28:19-20.)

_____

_____

21. What did Jesus do prior to His selection of the Twelve? (Luke 6:12)

_____

_____

Chapter Summary

OUR SPIRITUAL GOAL:
Let this mind be in you, which was also in Christ Jesus. (Philippians 2:5, KJV)

QUESTION:
How do you get to know somebody? Jeremiah 9:23-24 states the extreme importance of getting to know God. How well do you know Him?

THE MIND OF CHRIST

1. What did Jesus do OFTEN? (Luke 5:16) _____

Fill in the chart.

	Location	Time
Mark 1:35	_____	_____
Luke 5:16	_____	_____
Luke 6:12	_____	_____

2. Why did Jesus think it was important for Him to pray? (John 6:38)

_____

_____

Name two things gained through prayer.

Jeremiah 33:3 _____

_____

James 1:5 _____

What activities did Jesus perform after praying?

Mark 1:39 _____

_____

Mark 1:42 _____

_____

Luke 5:17 _____

_____

Luke 6:13 _____

_____

3. What character quality did Jesus show through His prayer life?

_____

_____

_____

4. What should you be doing to follow Jesus' example?

_____

_____

_____

PERSONAL APPLICATION

How can you improve your prayer life?

Plan an activity to accomplish this purpose, and then write down the specific steps you took in fulfilling the activity.

When did I pray?

For how long each time?

Where?

For what and for whom? (How about a prayer list?)

What happened? What change did I see in my life?

Footnotes
1. J. W. Shepard, *The Christ of the Gospels* (Grand Rapids, Michigan: William B. Eerdmans Publishing Company, 1939), page 115.
2. A. B. Bruce, *The Training of the Twelve* (Doubleday, Doran & Company, Inc., 1928), pages 11-12.

Chapter 6
THE SERMON
ON THE MOUNT

SERMON ON THE MOUNT

Locate the general area where the Sermon on the Mount took place. (Matthew 5:1-8:1)

_____

_____

_____

_____

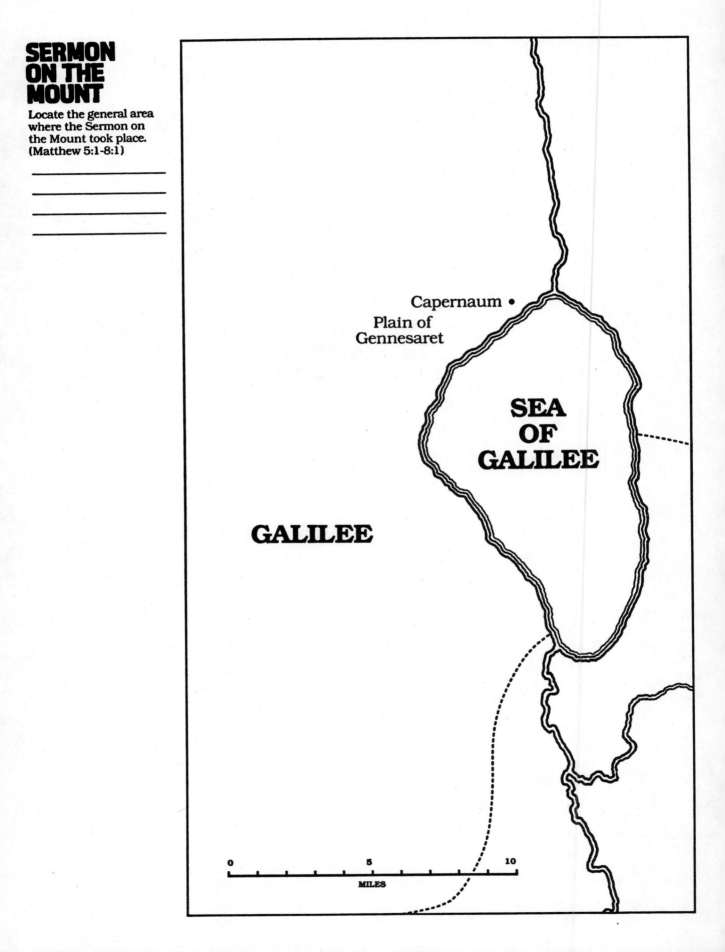

Capernaum •

Plain of Gennesaret

SEA OF GALILEE

GALILEE

0   5   10

MILES

THE SERMON ON THE MOUNT

But the wisdom from above is first pure, then peaceable, gentle, reasonable, full of mercy and good fruits, unwavering, without hypocrisy. JAMES 3:17

Bible references for this chapter
Matthew 5:1-8:1; Luke 6:17-49

After choosing the Twelve, Jesus began the discourse (a formal discussion) known as the Sermon on the Mount. The exact location where He gave the sermon is not known, but it is believed to have been somewhere between Capernaum and Gennesaret near the Sea of Galilee. Here Jesus taught His disciples and the crowds that followed Him. As He spoke on the principles of life in His kingdom—characteristics of those who would be His followers—*He disclosed the importance of attitudes behind a person's actions.* This *contrasted sharply* with the emphasis of the *Jewish leaders on outward performance.*

The Sermon on the Mount as recorded by Matthew was not a once-given teaching. Jesus probably gave the contents of this sermon many times during His ministry. Many of the points were repeated in different forms and under different circumstances. Luke, for example, records a short sermon given on the plains which contains parts of the longer sermon written by Matthew.

At this period of His ministry, Jesus laid down "a platform of important principles for the enlightenment and guidance of His kingdom forces. This sermon is not a mere ethical code but its sublime moral principles far surpass all human moral standards. Christ's idea of Righteousness as here set forth, became the kingdom's ideal of Righteousness which has never yet been approximately realized by humanity. In His universal eternal principles in this sermon, Jesus laid the basis for the kingdom work for all time. In one discourse, He superseded all previous standards and set up the new and final religious goal for the human race. He here uttered the final word about character and privilege, conduct and duty, religious ideals, the divine and human relations of men, and the supreme objective and goal in life and how to attain it."[1]

It should be emphasized here that the character and attitudes described by Jesus cannot be attained through self-effort but may be produced in a Christian only through the work of the Holy Spirit.

The Beatitudes

MATTHEW 5:1-16

DEFINITION:
The Beatitudes are "attitudes" that should "be" in your life.

The Beatitudes describe the character qualities that should be demonstrated in the life of a believer of Jesus Christ. Christlike character on the inside of a person will produce Christlike conduct on the outside. When the word *blessed* is used with reference to man, it means favored or happy. Each of the Beatitudes could begin with the words, "Happy is the man who is . . ." The Beatitudes were special declarations of blessings from Jesus.

1. To help you get a better grasp of the Beatitudes, fill in the chart below. You may want to use a commentary, a Bible dictionary, or a Bible encyclopedia to assist you in defining each character quality and promise.

The CHARACTER QUALITY described by Jesus	The PROMISE that goes with the character quality	Name a SPECIFIC ACTIVITY you can do this week to show this character quality in your life.
Define its meaning and relate it to yourself.	Define its meaning and relate it to yourself.	
VERSE 3 "Poor in spirit"	"Theirs is the kingdom of heaven."	If I accomplish something of merit, I will give all credit to Jesus because He gave me my abilities.
To have a humble and honest opinion of myself.	I will experience the glory and inner happiness of Christ's kingdom even here on earth.	
Verse 4 "Mourn"	"They shall be comforted."	
To feel sorrow for my sins and to repent of them (turn away).		
VERSE 5 "Gentle" (meek)	"They shall inherit the earth."	
To submit myself to God and to be gentle (self-controlled) toward everyone no matter what the circumstances.		
VERSE 6 "Hunger and thirst for righteousness"	"They shall be satisfied."	
To fervently desire Christ's righteousness (holiness) for myself.		

QUESTION:
What does Jesus say about you and holiness?

Base your answer upon 1 Peter 1:15-16, 2 Corinthians 7:1, and Hebrews 12:10.

The CHARACTER QUAL-ITY described by Jesus Define its meaning and relate it to yourself.	The PROMISE that goes with the character quality Define its meaning and relate it to yourself.	Name a SPECIFIC ACTIVITY you can do this week to show this character quality in your life.

VERSE 7
"Merciful"

To show compassion toward someone who has offended or hurt me rather than "getting even."

"They shall receive mercy."

OBSERVATION: Holiness is not an option. If you desire to have a close fellowship with the Lord, you need to be holy. See Psalm 66:18 and all of Psalm 15 (which describes a holy life).

VERSE 8
"Pure in heart"

To have a heart that is kept separated from all sin and seeks to honor God.

"They shall see God."

VERSE 9
Peacemaker

To restore peace when there is conflict.

"They shall be called sons of God."

The CHARACTER QUALITY described by Jesus Define its meaning and relate it to yourself.	The PROMISE that goes with the character quality Define its meaning and relate it to yourself.	Name a SPECIFIC ACTIVITY you can do this week to show this character quality in your life.
VERSE 10 "Persecuted for the sake of righteousness." To experience suffering because of my stand for "goodness" (doing what's right in God's eyes).	"Theirs is the kingdom of heaven."	
VERSES 11-12 Persecuted on account of Jesus To be insulated and evilly accused because of my stand for Jesus.	"Your reward in heaven is great."	

2. Jesus said that Christians are the salt of the earth (Matthew 5:13). What does salt do? How can you be "salt"?

a. _____

_____

_____

b. _____

_____

_____

c. _____

_____

_____

d. _____

_____

_____

3. Jesus said Christians are the light of the world (Matthew 5:14-16). How can you be a light?

a. (verse 16) _____

_____

_____

b. _____

_____

_____

MATTHEW 5:17-48

The True Meaning of the Law

Jesus then turned to the subject of the Law. His "teaching was so different from that of the Pharisees and Sadducees (which was supposed to be based on the Old Testament), that the people thought that He was undermining the authority of God's Word and substituting His own in its place."[2]

4. How did Jesus describe His relationship to the Law? (verse 17)

_____

_____

_____

5. Jesus then proceeded to enlarge the Old Testament teaching on the Law. Fill in the chart that follows.

OLD TESTAMENT TEACHING	JESUS' TEACHING	JESUS' APPLICATION TO YOUR LIFE	
VERSE 21	VERSE 22	VERSE 22	Verses 21-26
"You shall not commit murder."	"Every one who is angry with his brother shall be guilty" of murder.	I should not call anyone names, such as "You fool."	
		VERSES 23-24	
		If I have wronged someone, I should make it right with him or her before presenting my offering to God.	

	OLD TESTAMENT TEACHING	JESUS' TEACHING	JESUS' APPLICATION TO YOUR LIFE
Verses 27-30	**VERSE 27** "You shall not commit adultery."	**VERSE 28**	**VERSES 29-30**
Verses 31-32	**VERSE 31** "Whoever divorces his wife, let him give her a certificate of dismissal."	**VERSE 32**	
Verses 33-37	**VERSE 33** "You shall not make false vows, but shall fulfill your vows to the Lord."	**VERSES 34-35**	**VERSE 37**

OLD TESTAMENT TEACHING	JESUS' TEACHING	JESUS' APPLICATION TO YOUR LIFE	
VERSE 38 "An eye for an eye, and a tooth for a tooth."	**VERSE 39a**	**VERSES 39b-42**	Verses 38-42
VERSE 43 "You shall love your neighbor, and hate your enemy."	**VERSE 44**	**VERSES 46-48**	Verses 43-48

MATTHEW 6:1-8; 6:14-7:12

Having explained the relationship of His teachings to the Law, Jesus explained the motives and principles of conduct as applied to religious and social duties.

Motives and Principles of Conduct

6. Jesus said, "Beware of practicing your righteousness before men to be noticed by them; otherwise you have no reward with your Father who is in heaven." What three things did Jesus say to do in secret? Why? (6:1-18)

Verses 2-4 _____

_____

Why? _____

_____

Verse 5-6 _____

_____

Why? _____

_____

Verses 16-18 _____

_____

Why? _____

Note: At this point Matthew records the "Lord's Prayer" (6:9-13). Since it will be studied in another chapter, it is not discussed here.

7. What should your attitude be toward material things? Why? (6:19-34)

Verses 19-21 _____

_____

Why? _____

_____

Verse 24 _____

_____

Why? _____

_____

Verses 25-32 _____

_____

Why? _____

_____

8. What should be your primary concern?

Verse 33a _____

_____

God's provision? _____

_____

9. To which attitude in the Beatitudes does this passage relate? How?

Matthew 5:6 _____

_____

Promised blessing? _____

_____

10. Define "judging" as used in this context. (7:1-5)

_____

_____

_____

11. Why shouldn't you judge others?

Verse 2 _____

_____

_____

Verses 3-5 _____

_____

_____

12. Summarize what Jesus promised His followers.

Verses 7, 8, and 11 _____

_____

_____

13. How did Jesus compare a human father with your Heavenly Father? (Verses 9-11)

_____

_____

_____

Exhortations and Commands

MATTHEW 7:13-8:1

The sermon's conclusion tells how people of the kingdom might obtain the high ideals set forth. They are told how to enter this kind of life, whom to beware of, how to be genuine in their living, and why they need to build their lives on the solid rock of obedience to the Word of God.

14. Describe the gate to eternal life. (Verses 13-14)

_____

_____

Who is the gate to heaven?

_____

15. How would you describe good and bad fruit? (Verses 15-20)

_____

_____

_____

_____

16. The wise man built his house upon the rock so that when the storm came, it did not fall (verses 24-27). How is this a description of your life today?

_____

_____

_____

Chapter Summary

OUR SPIRITUAL GOAL: "Let this mind be in you, which was also in Christ Jesus." (Philippians 2:5, KJV)

THE MIND OF CHRIST

1. What principle was Jesus teaching the people through the Beatitudes? (Matthew 5:3-12)

_____

_____

2. Why was Jesus teaching these truths? (Matthew 5:20, 5:6)

_____

_____

_____

_____

3. How does Jesus judge our actions? (1 Samuel 16:7)

_____

_____

_____

4. What should you as a teenager be doing to follow Jesus' example in judging your own actions? (Proverbs 4:23)

_____

_____

_____

PERSONAL APPLICATION

Nine character qualities were described by Jesus in Matthew 5:3-12. Look back at the chart on pages 70-72 and decide upon one of the qualities that needs strengthening in your life.

Plan an activity and then write down the specific steps you took to strengthen that character quality.

Which character quality did I work on?

What specific action did I take?

When?

For how long?

What happened? What change did I see in my life?

Footnotes:
1. J. W. Shepard, *The Christ of the Gospels* (Grand Rapids, Michigan: William B. Eerdmans Publishing Company, 1939), page 419.
2. Arthur W. Pink, *An Exposition of the Sermon on the Mount* (Grand Rapids, Michigan: Baker Book House, 1950, 1953), page 49.

Chapter 7
OPPOSITION TO JESUS' MINISTRY

RISING OPPOSITION

Read each Bible reference and write in the name of the city or area where the event took place. Then locate and label it on the map.

You may use small arrows to indicate the travels of Jesus.

1. Last location from the previous chapter, where the Sermon on the Mount took place

   _____

2. Healing the centurion's servant (Luke 7:1-2)

   _____

3. Raising the widow's son from the dead (Luke 7:11-12)

   _____

4. Anointing by a sinful woman (Luke 7:36 and 44)

   _____

   _____

5. Opposition from the religious leaders (Matthew 12:22-24)

   _____

6. Teaching by parables (Matthew 13:1-2)

   _____

   _____

7. Stilling the storm (Mark 4:35-41)

   _____

   _____

   _____

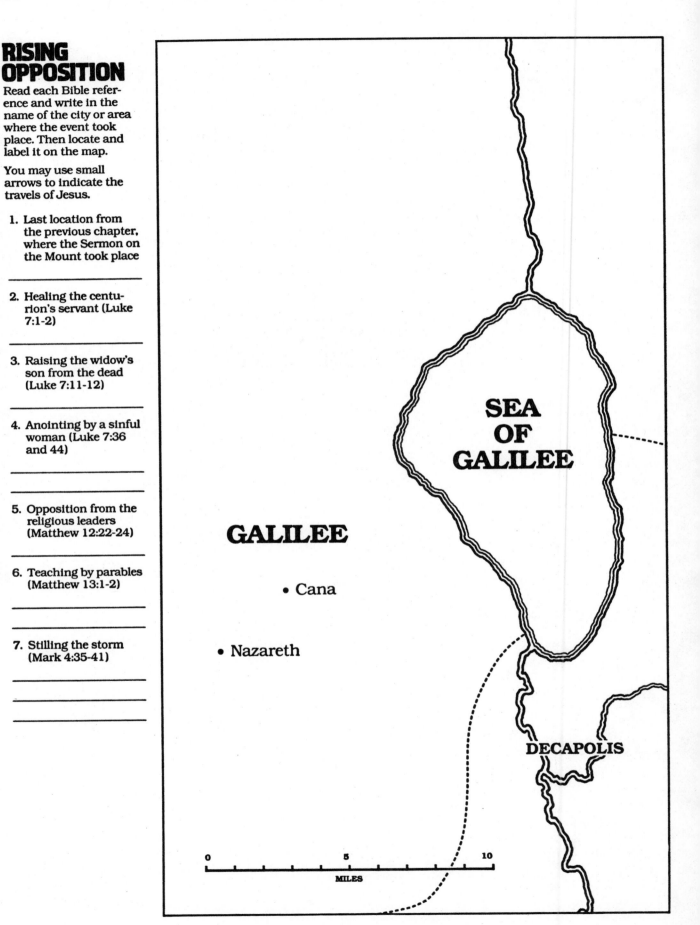

SEA OF GALILEE

GALILEE

• Cana

• Nazareth

DECAPOLIS

0   5   10

MILES

OPPOSITION TO JESUS' MINISTRY

I will open my mouth in a parable; I will utter dark sayings of old, which we have heard and known, And our fathers have told us. PSALM 78:2-3

Bible references for this chapter
   Matthew 8:5-13, 23-27; 12:22-13:53; Luke 7:11-8:3

Following the Sermon on the Mount, Jesus returned to the fishing village of Capernaum, where He had made His home. But again privacy and rest eluded Him, since many people came to Him to have their physical and spiritual needs met.

MATTHEW 8:5-13

Healing the Centurion's Servant

Jesus astonished His listeners with both the content of His teaching and the authority with which He spoke. As He walked down from the mount, a great crowd of people followed Him. When He entered Capernaum, representatives of a Roman centurion approached Him, asking Jesus to come and heal the centurion's servant. As the commander of 100 soldiers in the Roman army, the centurion was a man of authority. While the Jews hated most Gentiles, the people of Capernaum loved this centurion because of his many good deeds in the community.

QUESTION:
Why would a Roman soldier be kind to Jews?

1. Describe the centurion's display of:

Humility (Verse 8) _____

_____

_____

Faith (Verses 8-9) _____

_____

_____

2. How did Jesus use this example of faith to teach the multitudes?

Verse 10 _____

_____

Verse 13 _____

_____

LUKE 7:11-17

Raising a Widow's Son

Soon afterward, Jesus, still followed by the crowds, came to the little town of Nain, a few miles southeast of Nazareth. As He entered the city, a funeral procession of the only son of a widow passed by. The death of that son meant not only the loss of someone to care and provide for the widow, but also the end of the family name.

When Jesus raised the young man from the dead, He risked becoming "unclean" by touching the bier on which the corpse was carried. In so doing, He broke Jewish law and violated Jewish practice. "Certain procedures were practiced at Jewish funerals that were in marked contrast to the approach of Jesus. Mourners were hired to chant a lament. This was designed not as a comfort to the bereaved, but as a measure of the respect in which the dead person was held. There was little attempt to relieve the sorrow."[1]

3. What caused Jesus to act in the healing of the centurion's servant and the raising of the widow's son?

Verse 9 _____

_____

Verse 13 _____

_____

Reassuring John the Baptist

EXTRA STUDY:
What kind of person was this Herod?

OBSERVATION:
"The Expected One" was a term used by Israel for its coming Messiah.

LUKE 7:18-35

News of Jesus' activities swept the countryside, reaching even Herod's palace at Machaerus in Perea where John the Baptist was imprisoned. He had been in captivity for nearly a year and had begun to have doubts about the messiahship of Jesus. So he sent some of his disciples to Jesus to ask if He indeed was the promised Messiah. (Why John was in prison will be studied in the next chapter.)

4. What do you think could have caused John to question whether Jesus was "the Expected One"?

_____

_____

_____

5. How did Jesus answer John's doubts and help restore his faith?

Verses 21-22 _____

_____

_____

6. What did Jesus say about John before the crowds? What did He mean?

Verse 28 _____

_____

_____

_____

7. What does Jesus say about His own relationship to the Father? (Matthew 11:25-27)

_____

_____

_____

8. What do you think is the yoke and burden (load) of Jesus? (Matthew 11:28-30)

Yoke _____

_____

_____

Burden (load) _____

_____

Jesus' promise _____

_____

Are you willing to take upon yourself Christ's yoke and burden?

_____

_____

LUKE 7:36-8:3

Anointing by a Sinful Woman

Jesus, invited to a Pharisee's house to eat, was approached by a sinful woman while He was reclining at the table. This woman was neither Mary of Bethany (John 12:1-8) nor Mary Magdalene. She was "a sinner" (verse 37), a prostitute likely converted under John's or Jesus' ministry. The Oriental banquet was in a Pharisee's house. Guests reclined, so it was easy for the woman to wash Jesus' feet with her tears and anoint them.[2]

9. Why did the Pharisee react as he did to the woman's anointing Jesus? (Verse 39)

_____

_____

_____

_____

10. What was Jesus' reaction to her anointing Him?

_____

_____

_____

_____

11. What was Jesus teaching Simon in this incident? (Verses 40-48)

APPLICATION:
What is Jesus teaching
me through this
incident?

_____

_____

_____

_____

_____

Luke states that several women accompanied Jesus and His disciples on a preaching trip through Galilee (8:1-3). Touched by Jesus' ministry, these women now traveled with Him and the crowds and provided money for His needs along the way.

Dealing with False Accusations

MATTHEW 12:22-45

As Jesus ministered to the people, a blind and dumb demon-possessed man was brought to Him. Jesus healed the man, sparking a new round of accusations against Him by the Pharisees.

Though the New Testament says very little about the origin, nature, characteristics, or ways of demons, they are a present reality. In Scripture, the demon is an evil being, who belongs to the kingdom of Satan, or Beelzebub, and opposes God and His plans.

12. What must have been in the minds of the Jewish leaders that prompted them to make this blasphemous accusation?

_____

_____

_____

_____

13. What was the meaning of Jesus' reply to their accusation?

_____

_____

This encounter with the Jewish leaders marked a turning point in Jesus' teaching ministry. Because the leaders were now determined to destroy Him, He would shortly begin teaching in parables or coded messages which would be understood only by those who believed in Him and therefore had "ears to hear" (Mark 4:9).

14. What is the significance of Jesus' answer to the scribes and Pharisees after they demanded a sign from Him? (Matthew 12:38-45)

_____

_____

_____

_____

_____

15. As a summary to this section on opposition, in what ways is Jesus greater than

The temple? (Matthew 12:6) _____

_____

_____

_____

Jonah? (12:41) _____

_____

Solomon? (12:42) _____

_____

MATTHEW 12:46-50

Jesus' Family Seeks Him

While Jesus was being opposed by the Pharisees and was refusing to give them the spectacular sign they demanded, His family arrived and asked to see Him privately. Jesus had four brothers and at least two sisters (Matthew 13:55-56). Joseph was probably dead, and the family was now living in Capernaum where Jesus had moved them.

"These brothers were friendly toward Jesus earlier in His ministry (John 2:12); but after He was rejected in Nazareth (Luke 4:16-31) there seems to have developed in them a disbelief as to His claims; and later on they ridiculed Him, calling Him the 'Secret Messiah' (John 7:5). At this time they were unbelieving and indifferent as to who Jesus was."[3]

OBSERVATION:
Two of these brothers would later write New Testament books— James and Jude.

16. What did Jesus mean by His response concerning His family? (Verses 48-50)

_____

_____

17. Who is related to Jesus, according to this passage?

_____

_____

18. According to John 1:12, what is the Father's will?

_____

_____

_____

Teaching by Parables

DEFINITIONS:
A parable is a story used to teach some higher spiritual truth, or a parable is an earthly story with a heavenly meaning.

MATTHEW 13:1-53

Because of the opposition Jesus was now encountering, He began teaching by parables. Enthusiastic crowds still followed Him, so He climbed into a boat and taught them as they sat on the shore of the Sea of Galilee. What the crowds did not understand, Jesus explained to His disciples.

　　The parables of the kingdom, though not all spoken at the same time or publicly, give valuable information about the kingdom's origin, character, and development here on earth.

19. Fill in the following chart concerning this group of Jesus' parables. (Not every blank will necessarily be filled.)

REFERENCES/ TITLE OF THE PARABLE	TO WHAT DO THE MAIN FIGURES IN THE PARABLE REFER?	BRIEFLY STATE THE PRINCIPLE TAUGHT IN THIS PARABLE.
MATTHEW 13:1-23 The Sower and the Soil	The sower _____ _____	a. HARD SOIL Seeds fell upon the road; birds ate them. (Verses 4 and 19) _____ _____ _____
	The seed _____ _____	_____ _____ _____
	The soil _____ _____	b. ROCKY SOIL Seeds fell upon the rocky places; they sprang up but then were scorched by the sun and withered away. (Verses 5-6 and 20-21)
	The birds _____ _____	_____ _____
	Rocks _____ _____	_____ _____ _____
	Thorns _____ _____	c. THORNY SOIL Seeds fell among the thorns which choked them out. (Verses 7 and 22) _____ _____ _____ _____

REFERENCES/ TITLE OF THE PARABLE	TO WHAT DO THE MAIN FIGURES IN THE PARABLE REFER?	BRIEFLY STATE THE PRINCIPLE TAUGHT IN THIS PARABLE.
		d. GOOD SOIL Seeds fell on good soil and yielded a crop, some a hundredfold. (Verses 8 and 23)
MATTHEW 13:24-30 and 36-43 The Tares Among the Wheat	The sower The field The good seed The harvest The reapers The enemy The tares	Describe the kingdom of heaven as it is in the world today.

REFERENCES/ TITLE OF THE PARABLE	TO WHAT DO THE MAIN FIGURES IN THE PARABLE REFER?	BRIEFLY STATE THE PRINCIPLE TAUGHT IN THIS PARABLE.
MATTHEW 13:44 The Hidden Treasure	The man _____ _____ The treasure _____ _____ The field _____ _____	_____ _____ _____
MATTHEW 13:45-46 The Pearl of Great Value (Price)	The merchant _____ _____ The one pearl of great price _____ _____	_____ _____ _____
MATTHEW 13:47-50 The Dragnet, or The Parable of the Net	The dragnet filled with fish _____ _____ _____	_____ _____ _____ _____

Stilling a Tempest

MATTHEW 8:23-27

When He finished teaching the multitudes, Jesus told His disciples to sail across the Sea of Galilee to the eastern shore. This "sea" is actually a freshwater lake situated 700 feet below sea level in a valley surrounded by mountains. As cool air dropped down from these mountains, it often caused strong winds, high waves, and sudden storms.

20. Visualize yourself as one of the disciples. Describe your feelings and reactions as you live through this experience.

_____

_____

_____

_____

_____

THE MIND OF CHRIST

Chapter Summary

Reread the story about the centurion. (Matthew 8:5-13)

1. What did Jesus do in this situation? (Verse 13)

_____

_____

OUR SPIRITUAL GOAL: Let this mind be in you, which was also in Christ Jesus (Philippians 2:5 KJV)

2. Why did He do this? (Verses 8 and 13)

_____

_____

_____

3. What character quality did the centurion have which greatly impressed Jesus? (Verse 10)

_____

_____

4. How can you develop more of this character quality? (Read Romans 10:17.)

_____

_____

_____

_____

PERSONAL APPLICATION

1. Why is it so very important to have this character quality?

Hebrews 11:6 _____

_____

1 Peter 1:7 _____

_____

2. To whom are you going to show the character quality of faith?

_____

3. By what action?

_____

_____

2 Corinthians 1:20 _____

_____

Romans 4:20-21 _____

_____

_____

Using Question 3 as a guideline, plan an activity that will increase your faith in the Lord. Write down the specific steps you took in fulfilling this activity.

What action did I take?

When did I take this action?

For how long?

What happened? What changes did I see in my life?

Footnotes:
1. Donald Guthrie, *Jesus the Messiah* (Grand Rapids, Michigan: The Zondervan Corporation, 1972), page 98.
2. Merrill F. Unger, *Unger's Bible Handbook* (Chicago: Moody Press, 1966), page 524.
3. J. W. Shepard, *The Christ of the Gospels* (Grand Rapids, Michigan: William B. Eerdmans Publishing Company, 1939), page 219.

Chapter 8
EXPANSION OF
JESUS' MINISTRY

GROWTH OF THE MINISTRY

Read each Bible reference and write in the name of the city or area where the event took place. Then label it on the map.

Use small arrows to indicate Jesus' travels.

1. Last location from previous chapter

   _____

   _____

2. Curing the demoniac (Luke 8:26-27)

   _____

   _____

3. Healing Jairus' daughter (Mark 5:21-22)

   _____

   _____

4. Rejection of Jesus (Mark 6:1-2)

   _____

5. Sending out the Twelve (Matthew 9:35-38; 10:1 and 11:1)

   _____

   _____

6. Return of the Twelve (Mark 6:30)

   _____

7. Feeding the 5,000 (Mark 6:33-34)

   _____

   _____

8. Walking on the water (Matthew 14:22,34)

   _____

   _____

   _____

9. Discourse on the Bread of Life (John 6:59)

   _____

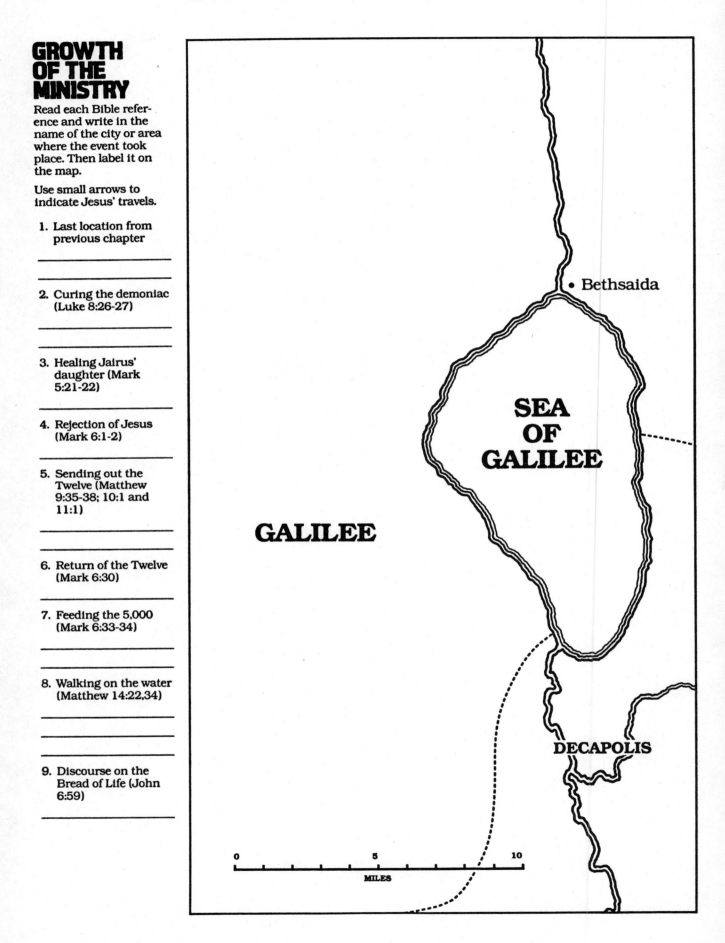

EXPANSION OF JESUS' MINISTRY

And all your sons will be taught of the Lord; And the well-being of your sons will be great.
ISAIAH 54:13

Bible references for this chapter
    Matthew 9:35-11:1; 14:22-36; Mark 5:21-6:44; Luke 8:26-39; John 6:1-13; 6:22-71

After the events of the preceding day, the disciples of Jesus were profoundly impressed. Here was One who in the same day had cured a blind and dumb lunatic, defeated the learned scribes and Pharisees in debate, taught many wonderful things in beautiful but hard-to-understand parables, and then with a word made the cyclonic winds cease and calmed the raging sea.

They were growing in their understanding of who Jesus was, but they had much to learn yet. He was not just an ordinary human named Jesus; He was also the divine Christ.[1]

Jesus now led His band of disciples into the non-Jewish territory of the Decapolis.

LUKE 8:26-39

Curing a Demoniac

Jesus and His disciples reached the eastern side of the Sea of Galilee near Gergesa. "Suddenly, weird terrifying shrieks rent the night air. Darting from behind the tombs, two demoniacs swiftly bore down on the little group. One of them was notorious and utterly uncontrollable. Men had tried using chains to tame him, but he shattered the links to pieces. His frenzied strength was phenomenal, and no one dared to pass where he lived. The disciples must have been terrified. . . . Or had their faith grown stronger since the stilling of the storm? . . . Surely the disciples were also overawed by the dignity and authority of Jesus as He stood facing the advancing demoniacs.

"Mark and Luke concentrate on the more notorious demoniac, but Matthew includes them both."[2]

1. Describe the demon-possessed man before and after Jesus dealt with him.

BEFORE (Luke 8:27-29) _____

_____

_____

_____

AFTER (Luke 8:35) _____

_____

2. Describe your life before and after you met Jesus Christ.

BEFORE _____

QUESTION:
*What would you be
like if you were not a
Christian? Would
there be a difference?*

AFTER _____ *(Answers will vary.)*

3. Why were the people of Gergesa so fearful? (Verse 37)

4. Why do you think Jesus did not take the former demoniac with Him?
   (Verses 38-39)

Raising Jairus' Daughter

MARK 5:21-43

After healing the Gerasenes demoniac, Jesus and His disciples returned to Capernaum by boat (Mark 5:21). As usual, the crowds were waiting for Him and welcomed His return (Luke 8:40).

Although most Jewish leaders were hostile to Jesus, Jairus, a ruler of the synagogue in Capernaum, asked Jesus to heal his dying daughter. Rulers of synagogues controlled the services. Their duties included the selection of who was to read from the Law and the Prophets and who was to preach. They also led discussions and generally kept order.

As He was following Jairus to his house, Jesus stopped to heal a woman. During this delay, the ruler's daughter died.

5. How do you think Jairus felt as each of the following occurrences took place?

MARK 5:22-24 _____

MARK 5:25-34 _____

MARK 5:35-37 _____

_____

_____

_____

MARK 5:38-43 _____

_____

_____

_____

6. What attitudes does Jesus want you to have in times of trials?

Verse 34 _____

_____

Verse 36 _____

_____

MARK 6:1-6

After Jesus raised Jairus' daughter from the dead, He healed two blind men and cured a demoniac (Matthew 9:27-35). Then He paid His last recorded visit to Nazareth.

Nazareth's Second Rejection of Jesus

7. Why did the Nazarenes reject Jesus? (Mark 6:3-4)

_____

_____

_____

_____

_____

8. What were the results of this rejection? (Verse 5)

_____

_____

What happens in our own lives when we reject Jesus' leading?

_____

_____

_____

_____

**Sending out
the Twelve**

MATTHEW 9:35-11:1

Jesus left Nazareth and went again among the cities of Galilee teaching in their synagogues, preaching the good news of the Kingdom, and healing every kind of disease and sickness (Matthew 9:35). At this point, He sent the twelve apostles out on a special assignment.

9. Jesus felt compassion toward the multitudes. Why? (Matthew 9:36-10:1)

_____

_____

_____

10. List the instructions given to the Twelve. (Matthew 10:5-23)

WHOM TO SEE (verses 5 and 6) _____

_____

WHAT TO SAY (verse 7) _____

_____

WHAT TO DO (verse 8) _____

_____

_____

WHY _____

_____

WHAT NOT TO TAKE (Verses 9-10) _____

_____

_____

WHY (verse 10) _____

_____

WHAT TO DO WHEN REJECTED (Verse 14) _____

_____

11. How does Jesus describe a disciple, including the "hard things" he will experience? (Matthew 10:24-42)

Verse 24 _____

_____

*QUESTION:
What does it mean to
"take up your cross"?*

Verse 27 _____

_____

Verse 31 _____

_____

Verse 36 _____

_____

Verse 37 _____

_____

Verse 38 _____

_____

Verse 39 _____

_____

After receiving their instructions, the disciples went out as Jesus had commanded them (Mark 6:12; Luke 9:6). Jesus Himself continued teaching and preaching in the villages of Galilee (Matthew 11:1).

MARK 6:14-29

Death of John the Baptist

About this time, Herod Antipas had John the Baptist beheaded. John had been imprisoned nearly a year in the dungeon of a fortification called Machaerus, east of the Dead Sea.

12. Why was John in prison? (Verses 17-20)

_____

_____

_____

_____

13. Why was he killed? (Verses 21-28)

_____

_____

_____

_____

14. Match Herod's actions (Mark 6:17-29) with each of the three areas of sin in 1 John 2:15-16.

a. The lust of the flesh _____

_____

b. The lust of the eyes _____

_____

c. The pride of life _____

_____

_____

_____

15. What did Herod think when he heard what Jesus was doing and saying? (Verses 14-16)

_____

_____

Feeding the Five Thousand

MARK 6:30-44   JOHN 6:1-13

The twelve apostles returned to Capernaum and reported their experiences while ministering in the cities of Galilee. Jesus then went with them across the Sea of Galilee to a quiet desert area near Bethsaida for rest. Instead of finding a place to rest, however, Jesus and His disciples were once again surrounded by the crowds.

16. Contrast how the disciples and Jesus reacted to the needs of the crowds. (Mark 6:30-44)

APPLICATION: How do I respond when I'm tired?

DISCIPLES' REACTION (Verses 35-36) _____

_____

_____

JESUS' REACTION (Verse 34) _____

_____

_____

(Verses 41-42) _____

_____

_____

Jesus Walks on Water

MATTHEW 14:22-36

The feeding of the 5,000 brought such a response from the crowds that they were ready to take Jesus and force Him to be king. Later that evening, Jesus went into the hills alone to pray and ordered His disciples to return to Bethsaida on the other side of the sea. But due to a strong wind which had come up against them, the disciples had, by three o'clock in the morning, sailed no more than three or four miles.

17. When the disciples saw Jesus walking on the water, what was their reaction? (Verse 26)

_____

_____

18. What caused Peter to sink? (Verses 30-31)

_____

_____

_____

19. What truth did the disciples begin to understand? (Verse 33)

_____

_____

20. What lessons do you think Jesus was trying to teach His disciples?

a. _____

_____

b. _____

_____

_____

JOHN 6:22-71

Discourse on the Bread of Life

After Jesus calmed the storm and the disciples' hearts, He and His men reached the northwestern shore of Gennesaret where He was again confronted by large crowds. Here He healed many people. He was concerned that these crowds were following Him from the wrong motive. They were more interested in physical bread than spiritual bread, meaning their salvation and a life of godliness. In His discourse on the bread of life, Jesus described Himself as the Bread of Life through whom a person may obtain eternal life, spiritual nourishment, and spiritual sustenance while still on earth.

21. At five points during this discourse there were reactions from the crowd. Indicate on the following chart the meaning of Jesus' words and the reactions of those listening.

WHAT DID JESUS SAY THAT CAUSED THE REACTION?	WHAT DID JESUS MEAN?	WHO REACTED? DESCRIBE THEIR REACTION.
JOHN 6:22-40 Verse 38 "For I have come down from heaven, not to do My own will, but the will of Him who sent Me."	_____ _____ _____ _____ _____ _____	JOHN 6:41-42 _____ _____ _____ _____ _____

WHAT DID JESUS SAY THAT CAUSED THE REACTION?	WHAT DID JESUS MEAN?	WHO REACTED? DESCRIBE THEIR REACTION.
JOHN 6:41-51 Verse 51 "I am the living bread that came down out of heaven; if any one eats of this bread, he shall live forever; and the bread also which I shall give for the life of the world is My flesh."		JOHN 6:52
JOHN 6:52-59 Verse 54 "He who eats My flesh and drinks My blood has eternal life; and I will raise him up on the last day."		JOHN 6:60-61
JOHN 6:62-65 Verse 65 "For this reason I have said to you, that no one can come to Me, unless it has been granted him from the Father."	JOHN 6:44	JOHN 6:66
JOHN 6:67-69 Verse 67 "Jesus said therefore to the twelve, 'You do not want to go away also, do you?'"		JOHN 6:68-69

22. Summarize Jesus' teaching about Himself in this discourse by explaining how Jesus is your bread of life.

_____

_____

_____

THE MIND OF CHRIST

1. Read John 5:30 and John 6:38. Paraphrase in your own words what Jesus said in these verses.

_____

_____

2. Jesus had a free will. He had the freedom to choose between doing His own will or His Father's will. He chose the latter. Why? (John 17:4)

_____

_____

3. What is the character quality shown by Jesus which we should be modeling in our own lives?

_____

_____

4. What can you do to show the heavenly Father you wish to be in His will? (Romans 12:1-2)

_____

_____

_____

Chapter Summary

OUR SPIRITUAL GOAL: Let this mind be in you, which was also in Christ Jesus. (Philippians 2:5 KJV)

QUESTION: Have you ever presented yourself to God as a living sacrifice as described in Romans 12:1? Verse 2 says not to be conformed to this world but to renew your mind. What steps can you take to do this?

PERSONAL APPLICATION

Think of one area in your life which you have not given totally to the Lord.

1. What specific steps are you going to take to give this area to the Lord?

2. When are you going to do this?

3. For how long is the Lord going to have charge of this area of your life?

4. Tell what happened as you followed your plan of action. What changes did you see in your life?

Footnotes:

1. J. W. Shepard, *The Christ of the Gospels* (Grand Rapids, Michigan: William B. Eerdmans Publishing Company, 1939), page 234.

2. Donald Guthrie, *Jesus the Messiah* (Grand Rapids, Michigan: The Zondervan Corporation, 1972), pages 110-111.

Chapter 9
FURTHER CLASHES
WITH THE PHARISEES

CONTINUED OPPOSITION

Locate and label (*using capital letters*) the major geographical areas of DECAPOLIS, GALILEE, PHOENICIA, and SYRIA.

Read each Bible reference and write in the name of the city or area where the event took place. Then locate and label it on the map.

You may use small arrows to indicate the travels of Jesus.

1. Last location from previous chapter

   _____

2. Controversy with the Pharisees (Mark 7:1-5)

   _____

3. Healing the Canaanite woman's daughter (Matthew 15:21, 28)

   _____

4. Feeding the 4,000 (Mark 7:31; 8:1-10)

   _____

5. The Pharisees demand a sign. (Matthew 15:39-16:1)

   _____

6. Healing a blind man (Mark 8:22-26)

   _____

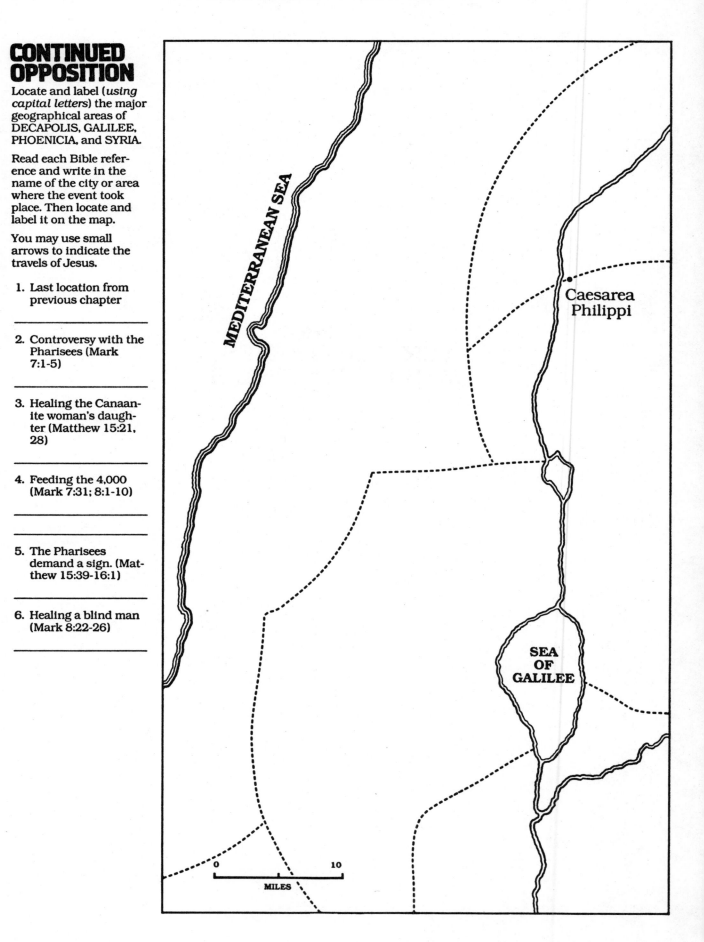

MEDITERRANEAN SEA

Caesarea
Philippi

SEA
OF
GALILEE

0   10

MILES

FURTHER CLASHES WITH THE PHARISEES

A bruised reed He will not break, And a dimly burning wick He will not extinguish; He will faithfully bring forth justice. ISAIAH 42:3

Bible references for this chapter
  Matthew 15:1-16:12; Mark 7:1-8:26

By this time Jesus had become well-known throughout Palestine and the surrounding areas. Although He was popular with the crowds, the religious leaders hated Him and created controversy whenever they could. As you study this chapter, look for reasons why Jesus was popular and for causes of the rising tensions between Him and the Pharisees.

MATTHEW 15:1-20   MARK 7:1-23

Evidently Jesus' ministry had caused a stir as far away as Jerusalem, because some Jewish leaders made the trip from the capital to Galilee to ask Him some questions.

1. Jesus quotes from Isaiah 29 in Mark 7. Why wasn't He concerned that His disciples observe the tradition of washing their hands? (Mark 7:6)

_____

_____

_____

What does 1 Samuel 16:7b say?

_____

_____

_____

How does this apply to us today?

_____

_____

_____

2. What is the difference between a commandment of God and tradition? (Mark 7:8 and Mark 7:3-4)

A commandment of God _____

Exposing Hypocrisy

DISCUSSION: Hypocrisy is one of our most common sins. We pretend to be "holy." We wear a front. What is yours? Is God fooled? What does 1 Samuel 16:7 say?

_____

_____

Tradition _____

_____

_____

Mark 7:7 says, "But in vain do they worship Me, teaching as *doctrines* the *precepts* of men."

The Jewish leaders were teaching the people their own rules (precepts) as though they were God's commandments (doctrines).

"Corban" was a term given to anything dedicated to the temple. Although it belonged to the temple, it could remain in the possession of the person who had made the dedication. As a result, a son might not support his old parents simply because he had designated his property or a part of it as a gift to the temple, calling it "corban." There was no need for him to turn over his property to the temple, but he was prohibited from ever using his property for the support of his parents.[1]

3. Why did Jesus rebuke the Jews for their use of the corban tradition? (Mark 7:9-13)

_____

_____

_____

What does Exodus 20:12 say? (Note the promise.)

_____

_____

_____

4. What was wrong with the Pharisees' attitude?

Verse 6 _____

_____

_____

Verse 13 _____

_____

5. How did Jesus respond to the statement that He offended the Pharisees? (Matthew 15:12-14)

Verse 13 _____

_____

DISCUSSION:
How do we treat our aged? What is our responsibility toward them?

Verse 14 _____

_____

_____

6. Why didn't the disciples understand the parable? (Matthew 15:15-16; John 14:26)

_____

_____

7. How did Jesus explain His parable? (Matthew 15:17-20)

_____

CROSS REFERENCE: Proverbs 23:7a

_____

_____

8. What commands of God might we tend to set aside by a current "Christian tradition"? How?

_____

_____

_____

_____

_____

_____

_____

MATTHEW 15:21-28

Healing the Canaanite Woman's Daughter

Jesus at this time withdrew to Tyre and Sidon. This territory and its major centers, immediately north of Galilee, were coastal cities of Phoenicia and a part of the Roman province of Syria. In this Gentile territory a Canaanite woman came to Jesus, seeking healing for her daughter who was possessed by demons. She begged Him, "Have mercy on me, O Lord, Son of David; my daughter is severely possessed by a demon" (RSV). It is strange that a Gentile should use the title "Son of David," a title referring to the promised Jewish Messiah.[2]

9. Why do you think Jesus went to Tyre?

_____

_____

10. Describe the attitudes shown by the woman.

Verses 22, 25, 27 _____

_____

Verse 23 _____

_____

Verse 27 _____

_____

_____

Verse 28 _____

_____

11. What was the attitude of the disciples? Why? (Verse 23)

_____

_____

_____

12. Describe how Jesus' attitude changed toward the woman.

Verse 23 _____

_____

Verse 24 _____

_____

Verse 26 _____

_____

Verse 28 _____

_____

13. What was significant about this event?

_____

_____

_____

Feeding the Four Thousand

MARK 7:31–8:10

"How long Jesus and His apostles remained in the borders of Tyre is unknown. Possibly the fame of the miracle forced Him to leave sooner than He had proposed. He did not return south to Capernaum, but took His way in a northeasterly direction, up through the region of Sidon. He likely followed the caravan road from the region of Sidon . . . to the south, in the borders of Decapolis, the territory of the ten allied Greek free cities."[3]

  Here the people brought to Jesus a deaf man who was also a stammerer. Taking him aside from the multitude, Jesus healed him. First He put

His fingers into the man's ears and touched his tongue with a finger moistened with saliva. Then He said, "Ephphatha!" meaning "Be opened!" The Gentile crowds were astonished at this miracle. As the news spread, the multitudes of these "other sheep" not of the Jewish fold increased. They remained without food for three days, sleeping on the ground at night and pressing to see and hear Jesus during the day. Because Jesus felt sorry for the people's hungry condition, He worked another spectacular miracle.

14. Compare the feeding of the 4,000 with the feeding of the 5,000. (See John 6:3-14.)

THE 4,000   THE 5,000

a. Place   DIFFERENCES

b. Length of time the multitude was with Jesus

c. Size of the multitude

d. Amount of food on hand

e. Attitude of the multitude after the feeding

f. What was left

SIMILARITIES

a.

b.

c.

d. _____

_____

_____

15. What principle concerning your life and ministry can you learn from the healing of the daughter and the feeding of the 4,000?

_____

_____

_____

_____

_____

The Leaven of the Pharisees

MATTHEW 15:39-16:12

From the Decapolis Jesus headed toward Caesarea of Philippi stopping along the way at Magadan (also called Magdala and Dalmanutha). There He used a discussion with the religious leaders as an opportunity to teach His disciples.

16. Why did the Pharisees and Sadducees ask for a sign? (Matthew 16:1)

_____

_____

QUESTION:
What were the main differences between the Pharisees, Saddu-cees, and scribes?

17. What was Jesus' response? (Verses 2-3)

_____

_____

_____

18. Explain what Jesus meant by the "sign of Jonah." (See Matthew 12:40.)

_____

_____

_____   _____

_____

The leaven used in biblical times served the same function as yeast does today. A small lump of dough called leaven was saved from every batch. The next time dough was made, this small lump was used to make it rise; then a new lump was saved for the next baking.

19. Why did Jesus compare the teaching of the Pharisees and Sadducees to leaven? (See 1 Corinthians 5:5-8.)

_____

_____

_____

20. Why did Jesus reprove the disciples for lack of faith? (Matthew 16:8-10)

_____

_____

_____

MARK 8:22-26

Healing a Blind Man

Mark records an additional stop in Bethsaida, en route to Caesarea Philippi, where Jesus healed a blind man in an unusual way. In some ways this healing resembled that of the deaf man at the Decapolis. In both cases Jesus took the men aside, used spittle, and told them not to tell others.

21. What was unique about this healing?

_____

_____

_____

22. What significance can be attached to this uniqueness?

_____

_____

_____

23. Why, in your opinion, was the man told not to tell others?

_____

_____

24. Give two reasons why Jesus healed people.

a. _____

b. _____

_____

_____

THE MIND OF CHRIST

Chapter Summary

1. The Pharisees asked Jesus why His disciples were not following their man-made rules. How did He answer them as He quoted the prophet Isaiah? (Mark 7:6b)

_____

_____

OUR SPIRITUAL GOAL: Let this mind be in you, which was also in Christ Jesus. (Philippians 2:5, KJV)

2. What was the great and foremost commandment according to Jesus? (Matthew 22:37-38)

_____

_____

_____

The number one character quality that we should be showing in our lives is *a fervent love for the Lord.* We should be loving Him with our whole being.

PERSONAL APPLICATION

---

1. List ways in which you can show the Lord that you love Him.

a. Tell Him you love Him—frequently.

b. John 14:15, 23-24 _____

_____

c. 1 John 1:3, 8-9 _____

_____

d. 1 John 4:20-21 _____

_____

2. Decide upon one of the above that needs improvement in your life. Plan an activity that will bring about this improvement. Then do it!

Answer the following:

What specific steps did I take?

When?

For how long?

What happened? What changes did I see in my life?

Footnotes:
1. William Baur, "Corban," *The International Standard Bible Encyclopedia* (Grand Rapids, Michigan: William B. Eerdmans Publishing Company, 1956), page 709.
2. Donald Guthrie, *Jesus the Messiah* (Grand Rapids, Michigan: The Zondervan Corporation, 1972), pages 158-159.
3. J. W. Shepard, *The Christ of the Gospels* (Grand Rapids, Michigan: William B. Eerdmans Publishing Company, 1939), page 289.

Alexander, David and Patricia (eds.). *Eerdmans Handbook of the Bible.* Grand Rapids, Michigan: William B. Eerdmans Publishing Company, 1973.

Baxter, J. Sidlow. *Explore the Book.* Volume V. Grand Rapids, Michigan: Zondervan Publishing House, 1960.

Bruce, Alexander Balmain. *The Training of the Twelve.* New York: Doubleday & Company, Inc., 1928.

Daniel-Rops, Henri. *Daily Life in the Time of Jesus.* New York: Hawthorn Books, 1962.

Edersheim, Alfred. *The Life and Times of Jesus the Messiah.* Two Volumes. Grand Rapids, Michigan: William B. Eerdmans Publishing Company, n.d.

Geldenhuys, Norval. *Commentary on the Gospel of Luke.* Grand Rapids, Michigan: William B. Eerdmans Publishing Company, 1951.

Gundry, Robert H. *A Survey of the New Testament.* Grand Rapids, Michigan: Zondervan Publishing House, 1970.

Guthrie, Donald. *Jesus the Messiah.* Grand Rapids, Michigan: Zondervan Publishing House, 1972.

Hendriksen, William. *New Testament Commentary: The Gospel of Matthew.* Grand Rapids, Michigan: Baker Book House, 1973.

Marshall, I. H. "The Gospel According to Luke," *The New Bible Commentary Revised.* Grand Rapids, Michigan: William B. Eerdmans Publishing Company, 1970.

McNicol, J. "The Gospel According to Luke," *The New Bible Commentary.* Grand Rapids, Michigan: William B. Eerdmans Publishing Company, 1965.

Mears, Henrietta C. *What the Bible Is All About.* Glendale, California: Gospel Light Publications, 1966.

Metzger, Bruce M. *The New Testament, Its Background, Growth, and Content.* New York: Abingdon Press, 1965.

Morgan, G. Campbell. *The Crises of the Christ.* Old Tappan, New Jersey: Fleming H. Revell Company, 1903.

National Geographic Society, *Everyday Life in Bible Times.* Washington, D.C.: National Geographic Society, 1967.

Orr, James (ed.). *The International Standard Bible Encyclopedia.* Five Volumes. Grand Rapids, Michigan: William B. Eerdmans Publishing Company, 1956.

Pink, Arthur W. *An Exposition of the Sermon on the Mount.* Swengel, Pennsylvania: Bible Truth Depot, 1950.

Robertson, A. T. *A Harmony of the Gospels.* New York: Harper & Brothers Publishers, 1950.

Sauer, Erich. *The Dawn of World Redemption.* Grand Rapids, Michigan: William B. Eerdmans Publishing Company, 1951.

Schaeffer, Francis and Edith. *Everybody Can Know.* Wheaton, Illinois: Tyndale House Publishers, 1974.

Scroggie, W. Graham. *A Guide to the Gospels.* Old Tappan, New Jersey: Fleming H. Revell Company, n.d.

Shepard, J. W. *The Christ of the Gospels.* Grand Rapids, Michigan: William B. Eerdmans Publishing Company, 1939.

Smith, David. *The Days of His Flesh.* New York: Harper & Brothers Publishers, n.d.

Stalker, James. *Life of Christ.* Old Tappan, New Jersey: Fleming H. Revell Company, 1909.

Stewart, James S. *The Life and Teaching of Jesus Christ.* Edinburgh: The Committee on Publications, the Church of Scotland, 1933.

Tasker, R.V.G. *The Gospel According to St. Matthew—An Introduction and Commentary.* Grand Rapids, Michigan: William B. Eerdmans Publishing Company, 1961.

Tenney, Merrill C. *John: The Gospel of Belief.* Grand Rapids, Michigan: William B. Eerdmans Publishing Company, 1948.

Tenney, Merrill C. *New Testament Times.* Grand Rapids, Michigan: William B. Eerdmans Publishing Company, 1965.

Unger, Merrill F. *Unger's Bible Handbook.* Chicago: Moody Press, 1966.

BOOK	CHAPTER	SECTION	MATTHEW	MARK	LUKE	JOHN
I	**ONE** **The Background to Christ's Coming**	The Messiah's Coming Foretold				
		The Threefold Office of the Messiah				
		The Deity of the Messiah				1:1-18
		The Ancestry of the Messiah	1:1-17		3:23b-38	
		The Geographic Setting				
		The Men Who Wrote the Gospels		1:1	1:1-4	
		Two Promises				
		The Promise to Zacharias and Elizabeth			1:5-25	
		The Promise to Mary			1:26-38	
		Mary Visits Elizabeth			1:39-56	
		John's Birth			1:57-80	
Census *c.* 5 B.C. Bethlehem	**TWO** **Jesus' Birth and Childhood**	Mary and Joseph	1:18-25			
		Jesus' Birth			2:1-20	
		Jesus' Infancy				
		Presentation at the Temple			2:21-39a	
		Visit of the Wise Men	2:1-12			
Passover *c.* A.D. 7 LUKE 2:41 Jerusalem		Flight into Egypt	2:13-23			
		Jesus' Youth			2:39b-52	
	THREE **Preparation for Jesus' Ministry**	John the Baptist	3:1-12	1:2-8	3:1-20	1:19-28
		Baptism of Jesus	3:13-17	1:9-11	3:21-23a	1:29-34
		Temptation in the Wilderness	4:1-11	1:12-13	4:1-13	
		Jesus' Early Followers				1:35-51
		Wedding at Cana				2:1-12
Passover *c.* A.D. 27 JOHN 2:13 Jerusalem	**FOUR** **Jesus' Manifestation to Israel**	First Cleansing of the Temple				2:13-25
		Discussion with Nicodemus				3:1-21
		John the Baptist's Explanation of Jesus				3:22-36
		Conversion of the Samaritan Woman				4:1-42
	FIVE **Authentication of Jesus' Mission by Healing**	The Geographic Setting in Galilee	4:12	1:14-15	4:14-15	4:43-45
		Healing the Nobleman's Son				4:46-54
		Rejection at Nazareth			4:16-30	
		Move to Capernaum	4:13-17		4:31a	
		Gathering Disciples				
		The Fishermen	4:18-22	1:16-20	5:1-11	
		The Tax Collector	9:9-13	2:14-17	5:27-32	
		Healing and Teaching Ministry	8:2-4 14-17 9:1-8	1:21—2:13	4:31b-44 5:12-26	
Passover *c.* A.D. 28 JOHN 5:1 Jerusalem		Discussion of Fasting with John's Disciples	9:14-17	2:18-22	5:33-39	
		The Sabbath Controversies	12:1-21	2:23—3:12	6:1-11	5:1-47
		Choosing the Twelve Apostles	10:2-4	3:13-19a	6:12-16	
	SIX **The Sermon on the Mount**	The Beatitudes	5:1-16		6:17-26	
		The True Meaning of the Law	5:17-48		6:27-36	
		Motives and Principles of Conduct	6:1-8 6:14—7:12		6:37-42	
		Exhortations and Commands	7:13—8:1		6:43-49	
	SEVEN **Opposition to Jesus' Ministry**	Healing the Centurion's Servant	8:5-13		7:1-10	
		Raising a Widow's Son			7:11-17	
		Reassuring John the Baptist	11:2-30		7:18-35	
		Anointing by a Sinful Woman			7:36—8:3	
		Dealing with False Accusations	12:22-45	3:19b-30		
		Jesus' Family Seeks Him	12:46-50	3:31-35	8:19-21	
		Teaching by Parables	13:1-53	4:1-34	8:4-18	
		Stilling a Tempest	8:23-27	4:35-41	8:22-25	
	EIGHT **Expansion of Jesus' Ministry**	Curing a Demoniac	8:28-34	5:1-20	8:26-39	
		Raising Jairus' Daughter	9:18-35	5:21-43	8:40-56	
		Nazareth's Second Rejection of Jesus	13:54-58	6:1-6		
		Sending out the Twelve	9:36—11:1	6:7-13	9:1-6	

BOOK	CHAPTER	SECTION	MATTHEW	MARK	LUKE	JOHN
Passover c. A.D. 29 JOHN 6:4 Jerusalem		Death of John the Baptist	14:1-12	6:14-29	9:7-9	
		Feeding the Five Thousand	14:13-21	6:30-44	9:10-17	6:1-13
		Jesus Walks on Water	14:22-36	6:45-56		6:14-21
		Discourse on the Bread of Life				6:22-71
	NINE Further Clashes with the Pharisees	Exposing Hypocrisy	15:1-20	7:1-23		7:1
		Healing the Canaanite Woman's Daughter	15:21-28	7:24-30		
		Feeding the Four Thousand	15:29-39	7:31—8:10		
		The Leaven of the Pharisees	16:1-12	8:11-21		
		Healing a Blind Man		8:22-26		
II	ONE A New Direction	Peter's Great Confession	16:13-20	8:27-30	9:18-21	
		Jesus Foretells His Death and Resurrection	16:21-28	8:31—9:1	9:22-27	
		The Transfiguration	17:1-13	9:2-13	9:28-36	
		Healing a Demon-possessed Boy	17:14-21	9:14-29	9:37-43a	
		Return to Capernaum	17:22-23	9:30-32	9:43b-45	
		Paying the Temple Tax	17:24-27			
		A Discourse by Jesus	18:1-35	9:33-50	9:46-50	
		Traveling to Jerusalem	8:18-22 19:1-2	10:1	9:51-62	7:2-10
	TWO Encounters in Jerusalem	Discourse on Living Water				7:11-53
		Mercy for an Adulteress				8:1-11
		Jesus' Teaching about Himself				8:12-59
		Healing a Blind Man				9:1-41
		Discourse on the Good Shepherd				10:1-21
		Seventy New Laborers			10:1-24	
		The Good Neighbor			10:25-37	
		Visiting Mary and Martha			10:38-42	
	THREE Ministry to the People Despite Opposition	Instructions on Prayer	6:9-13		11:1-13	
		Exposing the Religious Leaders			11:14-54	
		Warnings to the People			12:1—13:21	
		Feast of the Dedication				10:22-42
		Jesus and the Pharisees			13:22—14:24	
		Challenging the Multitudes			14:25-35	
	FOUR Jesus' Teachings in Light of Rejection	Three Parables			15:1-32	
		Teaching His Disciples			16:1—17:10	
		Raising Lazarus from the Dead				11:1-54
		Healing the Lepers			17:11-19	
		The Messianic Kingdom			17:20-37	
		Two Parables on Prayer			18:1-14	
		Marriage and Divorce	19:3-12	10:2-12		
		Jesus and the Children	19:13-15	10:13-16	18:15-17	
		The Rich Young Ruler	19:16—20:16	10:17-31	18:18-30	
		Rebuking James and John	20:17-28	10:32-45	18:31-34	
	FIVE Jesus' Triumphal Entry into Jerusalem	Events at Jericho				
		Healing Bartimaeus	20:29-34	10:46-52	18:35-43	
		Ministering to Zaccheus			19:1-10	
		Parable of the Pounds			19:11-28	
		Arrival in Bethany				11:55—12:1 12:9-11
		The Triumphal Entry	21:1-11 14-17	11:1-11	19:29-44	12:12-19
		Symbolic Events				
		Cursing the Fig Tree	21:18-19a	11:12-14		
		Second Cleansing of the Temple	21:12-13	11:15-19	19:45-48	
		The Visit of the Greeks				12:20-50
		A Long Day				
		The Withered Fig Tree	21:19b-22	11:20-26		
		The Question of Jesus' Authority	21:23-27	11:27-33	20:1-8	

BOOK	CHAPTER	SECTION	MATTHEW	MARK	LUKE	JOHN
		Three Parables of Warning	21:28—22:14	12:1-12	20:9-19	
		Three Questions	22:15-40	12:13-34	20:20-40	
		Jesus' Question	22:41-46	12:35-37	20:41-44	
	SIX **Continued** **Encounters** **and Teachings**	Warning to the Disciples	23:1-12	12:38-40	20:45-47	
		Denunciation of the Pharisees	23:13-39			
		The Widow's Two Copper Coins		12:41-44	21:1-4	
		The Mount Olivet Discourse	24:1—25:46	13:1-37	21:5-36	
		Prediction of the Crucifixion	26:1-5	14:1-2	22:1-2	
		Anointing Jesus for Burial	26:6-13	14:3-9		12:2-8
		Secret Meeting of Judas and the Leaders	26:14-16	14:10-11	22:3-6	
——————— Passover c. A.D. 30 JOHN 13:1 Jerusalem	**SEVEN** **Final** **Instructions** **to the Disciples**	Preparation for the Last Supper	26:17-19	14:12-16	22:7-13	
		Partaking of the Passover	26:20	14:17	22:14-16 24-30	
		Washing the Disciples' Feet				13:1-20
		Betrayal Foretold	26:21-25	14:18-21	22:21-23	13:21-30
		Institution of the Lord's Supper	26:26-29	14:22-25	22:17-20	13:31-35
		Discussion on Where Jesus Was Going	26:30	14:26		13:36—14:31
		Discourse on Bearing Fruit				15:1-27
		Revealing the Future				16:1-33
		The Great High Priestly Prayer				17:1-26
		Peter's Denial Predicted	26:31-35	14:27-31	22:31-38	
	EIGHT **Jesus'** **Sufferings on** **Behalf of Men**	The Agony of Gethsemane	26:36-46	14:32-42	22:39-46	18:1
		The Betrayal	26:47-56	14:43-52	22:47-54a	18:2-12
		The Jewish Trials	26:57 59-68 27:1	14:53 55-65 15:1a	22:54b 63-71	18:13-14 19-24
		Peter's Denial	26:58 69-75	14:54 66-72	22:54c-62	18:15-18 25-27
		Judas' Suicide	27:3-10			ACTS 1:18-19
		The Roman Trials	27:2 11-31a	15:1b-20a	23:1-25	18:28— 19:16a
		The Crucifixion	27:31b-56	15:20b-41	23:26-49	19:16b
		The Burial	27:57-66	15:42-47	23:50-56	19:38-42
	NINE **Jesus'** **Victory and** **Commission**	The Resurrection and First Appearances	28:1-15	16:1-11	24:1-12	20:1-18
		Appearance on the Road to Emmaus		16:12	24:13-33a	
		Appearances to Peter and the Apostles		16:13-14	24:33b-43	20:19-25
		Appearance to Convince Thomas				20:26-31
		Appearance by the Sea of Galilee				21:1-25
		The Great Commission	28:16-20	16:15-18		
		The Commission Repeated			24:44-49	ACTS 1:3-8
		The Ascension		16:19-20	24:50-53	ACTS 1:9-12

THE LIFE

and ministry of Jesus Christ clearly shows the purpose for which He came into this world—to bring sinful men back to God. The practical application of that great truth for a person who has never trusted Jesus Christ as Savior and Lord is to receive Him into his or her life.

The following is a simple gospel presentation, useful for Christians to share with others. It also shows the way to Jesus Christ, whose life and ministry you have just studied, if you have never received Him as your own Savior and Lord.

The Bible teaches that God loves all men and wants them to know Him.

But man is separated from God and His love.
"God is on one side and all the people on the other side."
1 Timothy 2:5, Living Bible

Why is man separated from God and His love?

Because he has sinned against God.
"Your iniquities have made a separation between you and your God."
Isaiah 59:2
"For all have sinned and fall short of the glory of God."
Romans 3:23

Where does this separation lead?

This separation leads only to death and certain judgment.
"Man is destined to die once, and after that to face judgment."
Hebrews 9:27
"Those who do not know God . . . will be punished with everlasting destruction and shut out from the presence of the Lord."
2 Thessalonians 1:8-9

But, there is a solution.

Jesus Christ, who died on the cross for our sins, is the way to God.
"God is on one side and all the people on the other side, and Christ Jesus, Himself man, is between them to bring them together, by giving His life for all mankind."
1 Timothy 2:5-6, Living Bible
"Christ died for sins once for all . . . to bring you to God."
1 Peter 3:18

Does this include everyone?

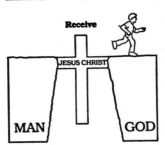

No. Only those who personally receive Jesus Christ into their lives, trusting Him to forgive their sins.
"Yet to all who received Him, to those who believed in His name, He gave the right to become children of God."
John 1:12

Each one must decide for himself whether to receive Christ.

Jesus says, "Here I am! I stand at the door and knock. If anyone hears My voice and opens the door, I will go in and eat with him, and he with Me."
Revelation 3:20

How does a person receive Jesus Christ?

Jesus said, "You may ask Me for anything in My name, and I will do it."
John 14:14

Therefore if you pray sincerely, asking Him—
> *Lord Jesus, please come into my life*
> *and be my Savior and Lord.*
> *Please forgive my sins,*
> *And give me the gift of eternal life*

—He will do it now.

If you have invited Jesus Christ into your life, the Bible says you now have eternal life.

"And this is the testimony: God has given us eternal life, and this life is in His Son. He who has the Son has life; he who does not have the Son of God does not have life."
1 John 5:11-12

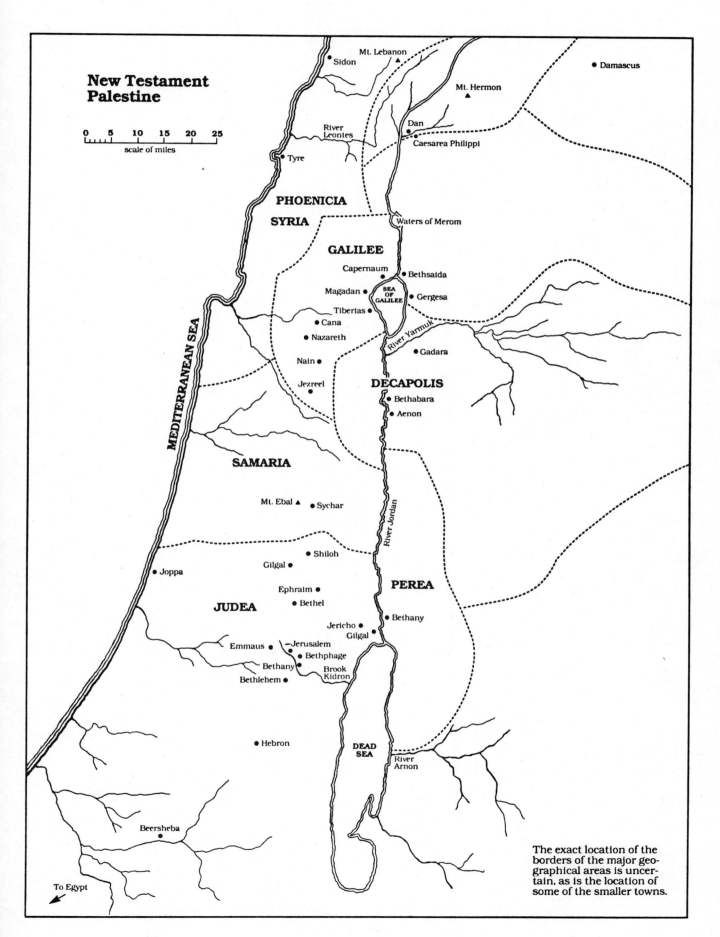

New Testament Palestine

0 5 10 15 20 25
scale of miles

PHOENICIA
SYRIA

MEDITERRANEAN SEA

Sidon
Mt. Lebanon ▲
Damascus
Mt. Hermon ▲
River Leontes
Dan
Caesarea Philippi
Tyre

Waters of Merom

GALILEE
Capernaum
Bethsaida
Magadan
SEA OF GALILEE
Gergesa
Tiberias
Cana
Nazareth
River Yarmuk
Gadara
Nain
DECAPOLIS
Jezreel
Bethabara
Aenon

SAMARIA

Mt. Ebal ▲
Sychar

River Jordan

Shiloh
Gilgal
Joppa
Ephraim
Bethel
PEREA
JUDEA
Jericho
Bethany
Gilgal
Emmaus
Jerusalem
Bethphage
Bethany
Brook Kidron
Bethlehem

Hebron
DEAD SEA
River Arnon

Beersheba

To Egypt

The exact location of the borders of the major geographical areas is uncertain, as is the location of some of the smaller towns.

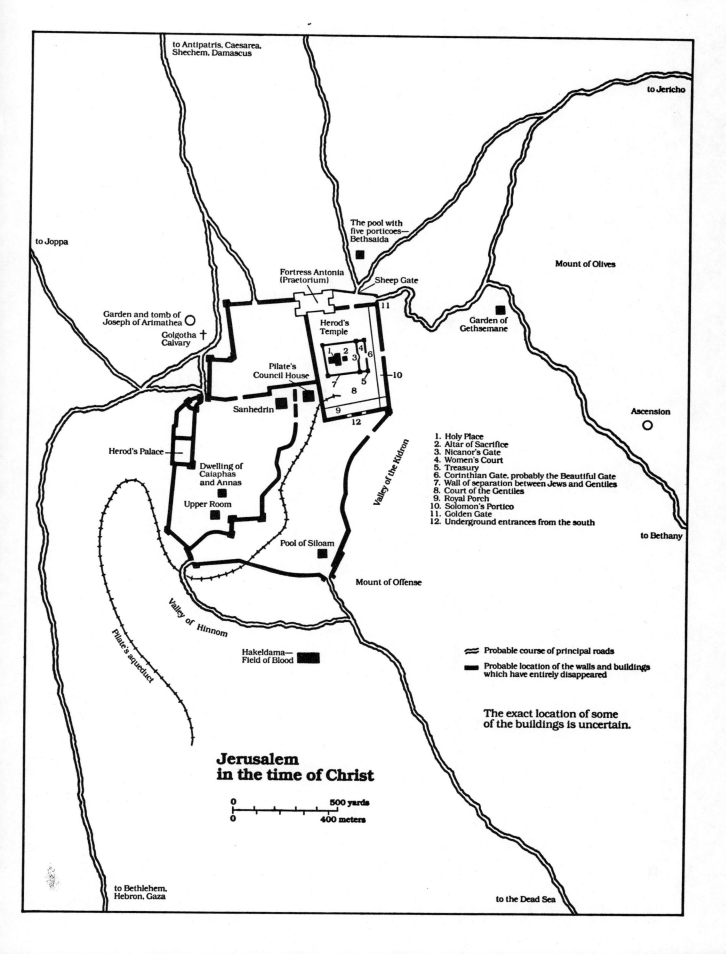

to Antipatris, Caesarea,
Shechem, Damascus

to Jericho

to Joppa

The pool with
five porticoes—
Bethsaida

Mount of Olives

Fortress Antonia
(Praetorium)

Sheep Gate

11

Garden and tomb of
Joseph of Arimathea

Herod's
Temple

Golgotha
Calvary

Garden of
Gethsemane

1 2 4
3 6

Pilate's
Council House

7 5
8 10

Ascension

Sanhedrin

9
12

Herod's Palace

Valley of the Kidron

Dwelling of
Caiaphas
and Annas

1. Holy Place
2. Altar of Sacrifice
3. Nicanor's Gate
4. Women's Court
5. Treasury
6. Corinthian Gate, probably the Beautiful Gate
7. Wall of separation between Jews and Gentiles
8. Court of the Gentiles
9. Royal Porch
10. Solomon's Portico
11. Golden Gate
12. Underground entrances from the south

Upper Room

Pool of Siloam

to Bethany

Mount of Offense

Pilate's aqueduct

Valley of Hinnom

Hakeldama—
Field of Blood

≈ Probable course of principal roads

■ Probable location of the walls and buildings
which have entirely disappeared

The exact location of some
of the buildings is uncertain.

Jerusalem
in the time of Christ

0   500 yards
0   400 meters

to Bethlehem,
Hebron, Gaza

to the Dead Sea